Check These *Assistant Engineers Handbook* Reviews:

This book is brilliant. A major achievement. Assistant Engineers Handbook is destined to become an industry standard.
Simon Andrews - Owner, Right Track Studios, New York

I've done a lot of sessions with Tim, and he was always great.
Bob Clearmountain - Producer, Recording Engineer

Assistant Engineers Handbook is filled with the information, techniques and standards which any assistant must have to make themselves indispensable, all done with a great sense of humor. Absolutely indispensable.
Frank Filipetti - Producer, Recording Engineer

No one is more qualified to author recording studio manuals than Tim Crich. This is a "must read" for anyone seriously considering a career in audio engineering.
Jim Vallance - Songwriter, Studio Owner

Full of solid information. Good job, Tim.
Recording Magazine

I am extremely impressed with this book. It has all the real world information that is sorely needed, but rarely (if ever) taught in engineering schools. Tim Crich has worked on tons of records including Rolling Stones, U2, KISS, Bob Dylan, Bryan Adams, even John Lennon. He has definitely been there, and here he tells all.
Josiah Gluck - Producer, Recording Engineer

Tim Crich's wonderful book fills a much needed niche in recording literature. Its common sense approach is informative and wise, while it keeps the reader chuckling. It is required reading here at Institute of Audio Research, as it should be for all aspiring recording engineers.
Merrium Friedman - Director, Institute of Audio Research, New York

(see over for more)

Assistant Engineers Handbook must be read by anyone considering a career in audio engineering. It should be mandatory reading for those already working in the field.

> Sandee Bathgate - Studio manager, Warehouse Studios, Vancouver

I hope all assistant engineers get their hands on this book. It is a true and proven guide to possibly the most undefinable job ever. I wish I could have had this guide to give to starting assistants at all the studios I've managed. I am very impressed.

> Bruce Levens - Owner, Greenhouse Studios, Vancouver

This book should be mandatory reading in every engineering school, and every assistant engineer, recording engineer and producer should use this as their bible. I'll bet if you read this book, you will be promoted in no time. It is worth every penny.

> The Music Paper

Tim's Assistant Engineers Handbook is the most informative and hilarious book I have ever read on the subject. I gave my son a copy, and told him to go and get a job.

> Ed Stasium - Producer, Recording Engineer

This well-crafted book is an indispensable reference for anyone aspiring to any kind of career in the recording studio.

> BAM Magazine

At last, a book effectively dealing with the psychology of session management. This book could save years of mistakes.

> Eric Vandersande - Vandersound Multimedia Schools, Australia

No other audio engineering manual I know of provides insight into demeanor, protocol, and prioritization in a professional recording studio.

> Carl Beatty - Associate Professor, Berklee College of Music

Quit bugging me.

> Bob Clearmountain - Producer, Recording Engineer

ASSISTANT ENGINEERS
H A N D B O O K

**The Definitive Guide to Working
as an Assistant Recording Engineer
in Today's Modern Sound Studio.**

Written and Illustrated by Tim Crich

BLACK ink PUBLISHING

Main Post Office Box 4295, Vancouver, BC, CANADA V6B 3Z7

ASSISTANT ENGINEERS HANDBOOK

PUBLISHED BY
Black ink Publishing
Post Office Box 4295
Vancouver BC CANADA V6B 3Z7
Tel: 604 632 3761 Fax: 604 732 9872 Site: www.aehandbook.com

Assistant Engineers Handbook / Written and Illustrated by Tim Crich

Canadian Cataloguing-in-Publication Data:

Crich, Tim
Assistant Engineers Handbook: The Definitive Guide to Working
as an Assistant Recording Engineer in Today's Modern Sound Studio.

Includes Index.

1. Sound-Recording and Reproducing - Handbooks, manuals, etc.
2. Sound-Recording and Reproducing - Vocational Guidance. I. Title

TK7881.4.C74 1994   621.389'3 C94-900297-6

ISBN # 0-969-82230-8

Printed and Bound in The United States of America

20 19 18 17 16

Editor - Tim King
Cover Graphics - Randy Paar
Technical Advisors - Ron Obvious, Bob Schwall

Without Grace, there is nothing.

CONTENTS AT A GLANCE

TABLE OF CONTENTS

. . . .

ASSISTANT ENGINEERS HANDBOOK

LIST OF ILLUSTRATIONS

ACKNOWLEDGMENTS

Grateful acknowledgment and a special thank-you to the following, without whose direct or indirect help this book would be... well... different:

Bryan Adams, Bob Clearmountain, Bob Rock, Bruce Fairbairn, Jon Bon Jovi, Gene Simmons, Frank Filipetti, Steve Lillywhite, Grace Mclean, Tim King, Bob Schwall, Ron Obvious, Paul McGrath, Rick Eden, Jeb Stuart-Bullock, Alan Friedman, Moira Marquis, Mark Hermann, Paul Hamingson, Warren Bruleigh, Mark Harvey, Josiah Gluck, Judy Reeves, Noah Baron, Randy Paar, Darren Grohn, Glenn Crich, Joan Crich, Matthew Crich, Buck Crich.
Special thanks: Mom for the tape recorders. Dad for letting me take them apart.

ANY IDIOT CAN GET GOOD SOUND

Any idiot can get good sound. This is a statement that was told to me by a great recording engineer (who shall remain nameless) while I was his assistant engineer on an equally great record (which shall also remain nameless.) While any idiot can get good sound, any idiot cannot be a great recording engineer. It takes hard work, dedication, talent, skill, luck and massive amounts of caffeine.

While it is not easy to *be* a great recording engineer, it is even harder to *become* a great recording engineer. The customary way is by starting at the bottom and working your way up to the top. Most of your time will probably be spent working as an assistant engineer.

Working as an assistant engineer is a wonderful job. You listen to great music all day, hang out with famous people, and work in an environment that looks like NASA's Mission Control. It's a knob twirler's delight. You get your name on lots of records, you get free concert tickets with backstage passes, and sometimes you get free meals. You even get paid — not much, but you do get paid.

Until now, there has been no manual, no guide, no handbook for the aspiring assistant engineer. This book is a compilation of notes, ideas and observations from my years as staff assistant engineer at the prestigious Right Track Recording Studios in New York City, and the legendary Little Mountain Sound Studios in Vancouver, Canada. In these studios, and a few more, I worked on thousands of sessions, including some of the most successful recordings of all time.

If you want to be a great recording engineer, you have taken a major step by opening this book. This is *the ultimate guide* for any newcomer who is serious about advancing in this very lucrative and satisfying field.

I want to make two points before we start:

First, there are many fine books available that explain the technical operations of recording studios. This is not one of them. This book is a practical, hands-on guide to help the assistant engineer with his or her daily duties in a recording studio. It's more like a driver's guide than an engine manual, therefore explanations of how the equipment operates are not included. I urge you to read all up-to-date books and magazine articles about the technical end of recording studios. You must have this knowledge to do your job properly.

Second, throughout this book I refer to the worker in the studio as "he" simply because it is awkward to say "he/she" all the time. I feel that anyone, male or female should have the same opportunities to rise through the ranks of the recording studio. To the vast majority of studio owners, producers and engineers, gender is not an issue. The only issue is the ability to do the job. Now let's get to the good stuff!

Tim Crich

CHAPTER ONE

. . . .

Getting Started

Welcome to Assistant Engineers Handbook — the only book available that is geared directly toward the assistant recording engineer. Remember that every song on every disk in every music store across the land used a recording engineer who was once a beginner. Every beginner needs a job.

GETTING A JOB

A diploma or degree from a recognized recording school, a good résumé, and experience go a long way in helping you to get a job in a recording studio. It's not like the old days when you hung around outside a studio until they finally asked you to come in and help with the engineering. With the high competition for jobs you have to show the people doing the hiring that you are serious about becoming a recording engineer. But don't despair. The increasing numbers of digital home and professional studios are producing a greater demand for qualified people.

SCHOOLS

Working in a recording studio is the best way to learn, but most people starting out simply don't get that opportunity. Schools are a great place to start in the recording industry because they offer beginners their first exposure to the basics of audio engineering and recording studio operations.

Many fine schools offer recording engineer classes. Some also offer courses in studio maintenance, artist management, record production, video post production, and a host of additional subjects covering almost all aspects of the music industry; some even offer classes on both résumé preparation and interview techniques. Some schools are affiliated with local studios and offer an internship program after graduation. Some offer cheap or free studio time to local bands for the students to practice their recording skills.

First, decide what your goals are, how long you want to attend school, and how much tuition you can afford. Then research the curriculum of the available schools. Then ask these questions:

- What level of education is required? Do you need a high school equivalency before being accepted?

- Does the school offer financial aid? Many schools try to help their students through government grants and loans.

- Are there on-site facilities, or does the school book time at a local studio for classes? Your tuition should go toward your education, not to a studio whose primary objective is profit. A school with an in-house recording studio will offer more hands-on experience.

- Have the instructors spent much time in a studio, or do they have limited experience? Teachers with experience in the studio are always preferable.

- Do you get transferable college credits for graduating?

- Does the school have a placement program? Some schools try to help the new graduate find work in local studios.

- Will the school give names of graduates for you to contact? If so, speak to the graduates and see if they were satisfied with the school's curriculum, the placement process, and follow-up programs, if any.

- Does it fit your needs? A six-week course cannot give you all the studio electronics, sound theory and musical instruction that a four-year program can. If you are interested in engineering, you shouldn't have to take any unrelated courses, such as managing bands.

Graduating from a recording school does not guarantee employment. Rarely does a studio hire engineers with no engineering experience, and it is unrealistic to expect a studio to hire you as an engineer just because you show them your diploma. No matter how much schooling you have, you will still probably start at the bottom as a studio runner. It doesn't take four years of schooling to learn how to make a fresh pot of coffee, but if making the coffee gets you into a recording studio, do it.

Schools can be great places to meet people and make connections, but they can't do it all. Sitting in a classroom and working in a studio are two entirely different things. In school, if you make a mistake, it's "No, *this* is how it's done." In the studio, it's "You erased the WHAT?"

RESUMES

Studios receive many résumés — make sure that the one they get from you looks professional. Go through the yellow pages and make a list of all eligible recording studios. Before sending your résumé, telephone the studio and find out the name (with correct spelling) and the title of the person doing the hiring, and the name of who you are speaking to. Mention the telephone contact in the cover letter, such as "I spoke to 'so and so' on this date, and she recommended that I send you a résumé." If you speak with the person who does the hiring, so much the better.

Send them two typed pages; one a cover letter, and the other a biography. Make them clear and neat, stressing experience over schooling. Chances of getting a job are better if you have some experience behind an audio desk (sometimes referred to as a console.) Follow up the résumé with a phone call to the same person. "I spoke to you on this date, and you told me to send a résumé. Did you receive it?"

Keep track of where, when, and to whom you sent all résumés, and what was said during the follow-up calls. Be persistent when calling studios. Don't take "no" for an answer. Send updated résumés and keep calling until somebody hires you.

EXPERIENCE

While applying at the local studios, try to get work in *any possible* audio situation. With the abundance of local bands and clubs, you should be able to find work, even if it's doing live sound free of charge. Get that experience whatever way you can.

Attend the industry trade shows, subscribe to the magazines, and go to equipment workshops that professional audio dealers often sponsor. The more you know about the studio system and its workings, the better your chances of rising through the ranks. As in many businesses, you keep up or you get left behind.

STARTING AS A RUNNER

Recording studios usually hire people with little or no experience as runners (also called interns or apprentices.) Runners are the beginners in the studio, hired to do the menial chores such as running to the deli, the stationery store, the post office, or other recording studios.

As a runner, you will also be a telephone operator, a doorman, a housekeeper, a receptionist, a delivery person, a waiter, a whipping post, and a host of other exciting career opportunities. The only time spent in the recording rooms is when bringing in equipment or food, or when helping the assistant with setup or breakdown. Runners often work long hours for very little or no pay, and are there primarily for the learning experience. This is a difficult concept for some people to understand, especially your parents.

Many of today's top engineers started out as runners. There are very few engineers who skipped the technical training and internship, and began as engineers. Typically though, you must work as a runner, then as an assistant before getting into the engineer's chair.

People often spend years working as a runner, expecting to get promoted, when they don't understand what is involved with the job. A lot of people drop out during this difficult period, not realizing the dedication needed.

The only way for a runner to learn is to hang out in sessions. During slow times in the day, and after checking with the engineer or assistant, go into the control room and quietly sit in a corner, This is where you absorb all the information possible. Talking, laughing and joking with the client out in the lobby is fine, but in the control room, keep quiet. If you don't understand something, ask the assistant when appropriate, such as after the session.

If you're good, you might occasionally work as assistant when the assistant works as the engineer on low budget or house projects. (Some studios strike a deal with an unsigned band by offering free studio time during off hours, with the studio reaping a share of any profits gained from record sales. This is called a house project.)

When you prove you can do the job, you may get promoted. You may even start to get paid. The smaller the studio, the sooner you can expect to be promoted to assistant engineer. In a major studio, it may take longer, but with perseverance, you will eventually be bringing coffee to first rate engineers and producers.

WORKING AS AN ASSISTANT ENGINEER

Somewhere between sweeping floors and sweeping equalization is the position of assistant engineer. The engineer is concentrating on getting the best sounds he can. The producer is concentrating on the music, the parts, and the arrangements. The band is concentrating on playing well. That leaves everything else up to the assistant engineer — you.

This is a job where the work is demanding. You really must know that this is the business for you or you simply won't last. Once you become an engineer, you can expect to make a very good living. But working your way up the recording studio ladder can be a difficult process. For years I was on the "New York Studio Diet" which consisted of three parts:

1) Walking 43 blocks to work every day.

2) Eating once every two or three days, whether I needed to or not.

3) Running 43 blocks home as fast as I could in the middle of the night.

You need to be very dedicated to the idea that one day you will be sitting in the engineer's chair.

HOURS AND WAGES

Long hours for the assistant engineer are legendary. Sessions are long enough as it is, but the assistant arrives earlier, and leaves later than anyone else in the session. As well as long hours, there is usually no such thing a weekend off — or making plans for next Friday night. Marathon weekend sessions are routine. In most jobs, after a regular shift is finished, a worker is relieved by another worker. Not so in the recording studio. Usually an assistant is assigned to a project, and stays with it no matter how many hours are involved.

The concept of day and night falls into some vast unknown void. When I was assistant engineer on Rolling Stones' "Dirty Work" it was not unusual to arrive at the studio around 11 or 12 at night. By 3 or 4 A.M. Keith Richards would stagger in, and the session would begin.

You can forget about having any sort of romantic relationship. The only people who really understand the commitment to these long hours are other people in the recording industry. And who wants to hang out with them?

The wages for assistant engineers tend to be quite low. So low that the bowl of fruit and pastries provided by the studio for the clients was often my only daily sustenance. The studio manager once said "I never thought of Keith Richards as the sort of guy to eat a complete bowl of fruit every day!" Little did he know.

DUTIES

Your job is to do everything required to keep the session rolling along smoothly from before everyone arrives, until after everyone leaves. You will do all the little things, and the rest of the session staff will concentrate on the music. Due to a lack of standardization from studio to studio, your duties may vary. In one studio, you may do all the machine alignments. In another studio, you may answer the phones and do all the bookings. A good assistant can vastly speed up the recording process. A bad assistant can bring it to a screeching halt. Overall the duties of the assistant include:

- Transporting tapes between the tape vault and the control room, changing reels throughout the session, and operating all tape machines.

- Setting up and breaking down all audio, musical and electronic equipment necessary for the session.

- Making all equipment changes, such as cables, patches, and microphones.

- Keeping track of the paperwork, including tracksheets, takesheets, tape labels, work orders, maintenance forms, notes, and a log of daily events.

- Helping the engineer, producer, and musicians with their many session needs.

- Keeping the rooms clean, stocked, organized and comfortable.

- Doing the best job possible to keep the session running smooth and on schedule.

ATTITUDE

Even if you do all the above, it still may not be enough. To get ahead in the session you must gain the confidence of the engineer and producer by being:

- Agreeable. No matter how well you do the job, no one will want to work with you if you have a bad attitude. Being agreeable is sometimes not an easy task when you spend hour after hour, day after day in the studio with the same people. Do the best job you can, though you are dead tired and facing another long day tomorrow. With the right attitude, the rest comes easy. Enthusiasm, confidence and professionalism will be recognized and appreciated. You should be good natured, but not to the point where the session is a joke. It helps to take a sincere interest in the outcome of the project.

  If you change employment from one studio to another, learn how the new studio operates, and do everything their way. Every studio runs differently, and each feels their way is the right way. Don't come in and tell them that they are doing this or that wrong. They mean it when they say "This is the way we've always done it, and it works for us." Every assistant can learn different methods.

- Knowledgeable. Understand everything about the equipment in the studio, including correct setup, use, and breakdown. Engineers rely heavily on the assistants to help them with unfamiliar equipment. Without understanding the workings of every piece of equipment in the studio, you can't effectively assist the engineer.

- A Hard Worker. You need to go the extra mile to be remembered. Give the extra touch to the session and make the engineer feel that he is respected. If you load the tape on the machine and walk away, that may be fine for most engineers. If you load the tape, find the correct spot on the reel, set up the desk, rewrite the strip, do the patching, and get the engineer a soda, you will be remembered and requested for future sessions, and perhaps recommended to other engineers as a good assistant. As in any job, you must apply yourself to get ahead.

- Organized. Keep the rooms comfortable, clean, and well organized, with everything you may need at your fingertips. Look organized, even if it is difficult to *be* organized. Put all the unused equipment away when you can. Everything has a home, keep it there. Remove all used cups, food wrappers and soda cans.

  Erase pencil marks and smudges off the equipment, except any settings marked, such as a favorite level. Keep all the papers and lyrics in order. You may not be totally organized, but the client should think you are. When the rooms are disorganized and untidy, people naturally become anxious. The more comfortable the rooms are, the better the atmosphere, and ultimately, the better the outcome of the project.

- Reliable. This is not a job where you can call in sick whenever you want. You are the person who runs the session, and without you there may be no session. During a large project, if the assistant is regularly late or absent he is replaced with someone more reliable. However, there are exceptions. During the recording of Bryan Adams' "Waking up the Neighbours" I was stricken with a kidney stone, and had to leave the session early. When I returned the next day, the band had recorded me a version of that classic Bob Dylan song, "Like a Kidney Stone."

- Well Read. Read as many books and magazines about the recording industry as possible. The more you know about the studio and its technologies, the better you will be equipped to do your job. Being well read gives you credibility. If a client or engineer asks your opinion of the new "Triple turbo super digital tube modulator," you should have at least a basic knowledge of its workings.

- Musical. Most clients would prefer to work with an engineering staff that has a musical background. After all, this is the music business. If you don't own a musical instrument, get one and learn the basics, at least enough to recognize chords and notes when you see or hear them being played. Being able to play a musical instrument gives you a major advantage over someone who doesn't. Playing a musical instrument will get you a sense of tuning, a feel for timing, and lots of babes.

- Discreet. Sometimes you are involved in the session, helping with suggestions and ideas, and sometimes you simply blend into the woodwork. A good assistant is like a good waiter at a fine restaurant. He is not always noticed, but everything is quietly taken care of. Discretion dictates when and when not to be noticed.

  Keep the vibe of the session up. Clients want to feel that the engineer is in complete control. If you are working with an engineer who has made a mistake in the past, don't bring that up. If clients hear how he erased something on a different project, they will not have full confidence in him. They want to concentrate totally on the music, not on whether the engineer is going to accidentally erase something. Make them feel that they are getting a reliable studio and staff.

  Think before speaking. What may be a revelation to you may be obvious to an experienced engineer. Don't start adding your little ideas or offerings to the session unless you are absolutely positively sure you have something beneficial to contribute.

  Don't bad mouth your studio, your co-workers or any engineers. The recording community is surprisingly small, and these things may return to haunt you.

- Hygienic. You will be stuck in a small room, for hours upon hours, working closely with your colleagues. When you are in a marathon session, every once in a while take a quick break to refresh yourself by splashing your face with water. Carry a toothbrush with you, and use it. You will look better, feel better and smell better. Not wearing a clean shirt may be the fad this week, but it doesn't encourage clients to return to your studio. As we all know, it can be uncomfortable to be stuck working next to a person who doesn't realize he has an odor problem.

DEALING WITH...

Being an assistant engineer involves not only working with electronic equipment, but also dealing with people. These people are:

RECORDING ENGINEERS

Most engineers work in various recording studios, and with many different assistant engineers. If the engineer likes you and the way you work, he may want to use you on all of his sessions. With a good rapport between you and the engineer, the sessions should be smooth and trouble free.

The only way to do the best job possible is to learn from all the engineers you work with. Most engineers are happy to show the eager assistant why he uses, for instance, a certain delay, or favorite special effect. If you get on well with the engineer, you can ask him questions about his methods of recording that you might not feel comfortable asking other engineers.

To do your job, you must learn as much as possible about different methods of recording. Each engineer has different tricks and ways of doing things, and each feels that his way is correct. Write down any new methods or techniques of recording used by different engineers. This will be very helpful when you start engineering. However, don't divulge one engineer's secrets to another engineer. Just use them yourself.

If you like a certain engineer and how he works, don't be afraid to request working with him on all his sessions at your studio. Clear this with him and with the studio manager. Unless the engineer really doesn't like you, this should not be a problem.

The best way to work with your favorite engineer is to do such a great job that he requests you whenever he works at your studio. If you always do a good job, he may give you a certain degree of freedom, such as letting you do some of the edits, or set up some sounds, or perhaps even do a bit of the engineering.

Another good reason to get to know an engineer and do a good job for him is that if he gets into production, he will be looking for an engineer to replace himself. This is a perfect opportunity for you, because he knows you, knows how you work, and knows that you do a good job. This is called getting ahead in the recording industry.

PRODUCERS

The definition of a record producer is certainly vague. He is usually the person responsible for the final product. Some producers take care of all financial dealings, including equipment rentals, musician fees, tapes, studio costs, etc. Some will also help write the songs, do the arrangements, play the instruments, and do all the engineering. A good producer realizes each musician, project and session needs to be approached differently. Methods of getting the best performance out of one artist may not work for another. He also knows when to push the artist a bit more, when he has the best performance recorded, when it's time to move on, and when to tell the difference.

Most of today's more popular producers are very patient and talented people who do a good job and deserve their success. However, there is the occasional producer who spends all day on the telephone, occasionally interrupting his conversation to say to the band, "Yeah, sounds great, you guys are gonna be stars. Any sushi left?"

Producers, being in charge of the project, have been known to take advantage of the lowly assistant engineer, like having him get their dry cleaning or wash their car, or shaving some time off the studio bill. You work harder than anyone else in the session, so do not let them take advantage of you. Mind you, giving them an extra fifteen minutes occasionally, just enough to endear yourself to them, may not hurt.

Don't argue with the producer. He usually has the highest priority in the studio. Try to get along with him, no matter how difficult or unreasonable he may be. Of course, if he wants to record the sound of the control room window smashing for the band's next hit single, you might want to step in and discuss it with him.

CLIENTS AND ARTISTS

The clients are the whole reason you are working. They are paying the bills, so ultimately they are the ones who must be satisfied. I once worked with a singer who was not happy singing into a small microphone the engineer preferred. He felt he was so talented he needed a large microphone, not a wimpy little one. The engineer realized that since the singer was paying the bills he was the boss. The engineer had me change microphones from the high quality smaller microphone to a larger, albeit lower quality, microphone. That lesson taught me that the client is always right.

The clients, however, aren't always the musicians. With jingles, for example, they might be an advertising agency. For a record project, they might be the record company. For a demo, they might be the musicians. Usually, in the studio, everyone involved in the session besides the engineering staff is referred to as the client. Whoever the clients are, they are using your studio because they want predictable results. The assistant is usually provided by the studio to assure that the clients get what they want.

From the time they arrive to the time they leave, the clients should be comfortable and happy. This means you show them their location in the studio and help them with their instruments. They will need help with anything and everything that needs to be set up, plugged in, taped, wired, adjusted, added, removed, or simply twiddled with. Make the clients feel that the studio staff involved in their project are very qualified.

Throughout the session, if anyone is having any problems at all, go out and help. If a musician removes his headphones to change or adjust them, or if he begins to change the microphone stand, go out and make the change. He is not there to fix or adjust anything. This is *your* job. When he sees you coming out to help, the next time he wants something changed, rather than doing it himself, he will just call you. Your goal is to make the clients feel comfortable enough to want to return to your studio for future projects. When dealing with clients, here are a few guidelines:

- Don't stop musicians when they are in the middle of jamming unless you really need to. It is not your place. Musicians tend to get "in the groove" while playing, and they might not appreciate being interrupted by the lowly assistant. Leave that to the engineer or producer.

- Avoid singing your own little versions of the songs you are working on. Imagine how impressed George Martin would have been had he heard the assistant engineer singing "All You Need Is Lunch."

- Be especially careful when joking with clients. Although most sessions seem casual, a lot of money, time, and hard work is involved. No one thinks jokes about erasing a track, or not being in *record* during a great take are funny. It can be disheartening to the musicians if, after a great take, the assistant jokingly says, "Oh, I guess we should have recorded that, nyuk, nyuk." It may seem hilarious to you, but it shows your studio inexperience.

- Don't mention how much their song reminds you of another song. Every songwriter likes to feel his work is somewhat original, not just a re-hash of someone else's music.

- No matter how terrible you think a song is, when they ask you your opinion, don't say "Man, that really stinks." A good assistant engineer must be diplomatic. On the other end of the scale, don't rave on about how great it is when everyone knows it isn't. Most musicians know when they are being stroked. If they ask you your opinion, give them the truth, and you will get more respect in the long term. Try to be positive, even if it's "Hey, I really dig that high-hat." If you don't have an opinion, get one.

- Try to befriend the clients. If they like you and the way you work, they may want to return to your studio for their next project — perhaps even use you to engineer.

- Often *you* are the only representative of the studio in the session. Sometimes the clients may get annoyed at the studio, and come down on you. Alas, sometimes your job pits you between management and clients. The clients may take their frustrations with the studio out on you, and management at times gets on you for the client's behavior in the studio. When it comes right down to it, a good studio will side with the assistant.

- Being in a small room for great lengths of time may create friction between people. When arguments arise — and they will — stay out of it. It is not your place to step in and try to ease the situation unless the studio is threatened. If the situation comes to blows then, as always, punch the littlest guy.

STUDIO MANAGERS

Generally the studio manager is the person who books the studio, does the hiring and firing, and keeps the whole place in order. He may be an owner, an engineer, both, or neither. The manager is linked to the studio by the assistant engineers, and can only run a studio well if he knows what is going on within the actual sessions.

Give him clear legible paperwork, and keep him informed of tape and equipment used, down time or schedule changes. He shouldn't be the last to know that the project being worked on is going to run two weeks over schedule.

Keep the manager happy. If he isn't happy with the way you work, you may not end up working on the best projects that come in. There really isn't anything wrong working on the next "Polka Pals 'n Gals" record, but you probably want to do projects with a little more exposure.

. . . .

Summary

Chapter One explained what is required to get started in the recording industry:

- How to prepare for getting a job in the recording studio, including résumé preparation, looking for a job and applying at different recording studios.

- What is involved in being a runner.

- What is expected of a good assistant engineer, including the dedication needed, the hours and wages, the duties, and the right attitude.

- How to deal with the people in the recording studio, including the recording engineers, record producers, clients and musicians, and studio managers.

CHAPTER TWO

. . . .

Setting Up The Studio

Recording studios do much more than record the pop songs we hear on the radio. The spoken word, sound effects, jingles, and film and television soundtracks are very much a part of the recording industry. Although this book is mainly laid out for sessions involving musical instruments, it can be adapted to any specific application not directly related to music. References to the musician may be adapted to any non-music related artists, such as voice over announcers.

Methods of setup and recording vary widely from engineer to engineer and from studio to studio, so it is not possible to detail all situations you may encounter. Some recording studios leave the musical instruments set up, so breakdown isn't required after each session. Other studios have house instruments such as drums, pianos, guitars and amplifiers that are used for every session.

Basic tracks, simply called basics, are the first, or primary instruments to be recorded. (See Chapter Eight for more on basics.) Overdubs are then dubbed over, or recorded along with the basics to finish with a final complete passage of music. (See Chapter Ten for more on overdubs.) Whether doing basics or overdubs, setting up the instruments is generally the same. The only differences are placement of the musical instrument or musician, and the amount of setup time required. Setup for a large or complex basic session may take up to a couple of hours, while setup for an overdub session should take no longer than an hour. Instruments tend to be set up and recorded individually for overdubs.

Note that the term *recording studio* usually covers the complete building or business. When referring to the individual rooms, usually the *studio* is where the musicians play the music, and the *control room* is where the engineer records it.

BEFORE STARTING THE SETUP

Find out the scheduled start time, and judge when to arrive to begin setting up. Leave a little more time than you think you need in case the setup takes longer than planned. If you are responsible for the tape machine alignments, arrive even earlier. The ideal situation would have the technical staff do the alignments, leaving the assistant free to do the setup of the studio and control room. (See Chapter Four for more on alignments.) When setting up for a large session, try to bring in a runner to help set up and check the equipment.

When a large session is scheduled to begin in the morning, try to do some of the setup the night before, rather than arrive at some ridiculously early hour. If overdubs or mixes are taking place in the control room the night before, the studio may be available for cleaning and setting up equipment. Before going in, ask the engineer for permission. Do not ask the client. Some clients may feel that they are paying for the whole recording studio, and they don't want anyone setting up for another session on their time. If the studio is not in use the night before, check with the studio manager before going in.

SUPPLIES

Keep the control room and studio neat and tidy with all supplies organized and close at hand. You might want to have your own personal collection of some of the following smaller items. They should include:

- Pens, pencils, china markers or grease pencils (various colors), Sharpie felt pens (various colors), and pads of writing paper. Engineers seem to have this thing about sharp pencils, so put at least one on or near the desk.

- Unused paperwork, like blank tracksheets, takesheets, tape labels, and maintenance forms. You should never have to hunt around for any important forms in the middle of a session. A three-hole punch helps keep all paperwork organized in the daily log. (See Chapter Seven for more on the daily log.)

- Razor blades, splicing tape, and leader tape for edits and assembly. Different engineers may prefer paper to plastic leader tape, or different widths of splicing tape. Also keep cotton swabs, isopropyl alcohol, rubber cleaner, tissues, an alignment tool, a head demagnetizer, and a few empty reels.

- Various kinds of adhesive tape. Red and blue ¼" adhesive tape is sometimes used for taping the ends of a reel of tape to the reel. White adhesive tape is often used when writing the strip on the desk. (See Chapter Six for more on the scribble strip.) Avoid using conventional masking tape as it leaves a sticky film wherever it is used. Leave a few rolls of duct tape around the studio for anyone to grab and use. Hide a roll away somewhere so you'll always have one in an emergency.

- Enough power. Place all electrical extension cords and boxes in a convenient place. As well, the studio should keep a supply of batteries of various voltages.

- A flashlight, in case you need to go behind equipment to check connections.

- Plenty of paper towels and tissue boxes throughout the control room and studio.

- The manuals of any new or rental equipment with which you or the engineer might not be familiar.

- Packing blankets, sand bags and small carpets nearby in the studio for use during setup. Set out enough ashtrays and matches for those poor souls who still smoke.

ENVIRONMENTS IN THE ROOMS

- Lighting in the studio can be very important when musicians are trying to create. Change burnt out light bulbs in the control room and studio. If applicable, replace them with the same color bulbs.

- Keep the rooms comfortably cool. Wide changes in temperature may cause some musical instruments to go out of tune. As well, understand the serious consequences of leaving the air conditioner off, or the heater on high overnight.

  If you or someone in the session feels the temperature needs adjusting, change it by a few degrees, not all the way up or all the way off. If the air conditioner cuts out, the excessive heat in the control room can cause the internal workings of some expensive studio equipment to go into thermo-nuclear meltdown, losing all settings and custom programs.

- Sweep or vacuum the control room and studio thoroughly, empty all trash cans and replace the liners. Any equipment from other sessions, such as road cases must be put elsewhere for storage.

- Keep all chairs with wheels and door hinges well oiled. Entry to the control room and studio should be silent, not squeaky. Sometimes people like to enter and leave without being heard.

POWER UP

Before beginning any setup, turn on all the equipment. Start with the desk, if necessary, then turn on the tape machines, the outboard equipment, and finally the power amplifiers that drive the cue systems, and the studio and control room monitors. (Some studios leave the desk and amplifiers on all the time.) Power amplifiers are always the last to be turned on before the session, and first to be turned off at the end of the day. Before turning anything on, mute the desk's master gain in the control room and all sends to the headphones. The power spike from the amplifiers being turned on may blow the elements in speakers and headphones. Never turn a power amplifier on or off while anyone is wearing headphones. This gives new meaning to the term "getting one's ears pierced."

INPUT/SETUP SHEETS

The information on this input/setup sheet will be referred to throughout this manual to set up the studio and control room for the engineer. Figure 2.1. This is only an example, and is not the only way to do the job. Session procedures vary widely from studio to studio.

The engineer will leave an input/setup sheet indicating what instruments will be used, his choice of microphones and their inputs to the desk. Also included will be how he wants the desk set up, including busses and cue sends. (See Chapter Six for more on busses and cue sends.) Sometimes effects sends and returns, and outboard equipment are indicated. Any equipment rentals, different machine alignments, and other specific details regarding setup also may be included.

If the engineer doesn't contact the studio with the session information, telephone him. If you can't reach him, set up the equipment as best you can. If needed, call a senior assistant for help. Avoid doing nothing. An inaccurate setup is better than no setup. If the engineer is a regular at your studio, he may leave a stock input/setup sheet with the specific setups he uses.

Before any large setup begins, make a few photocopies of the input/setup sheet. Leave copies in the studio and the control room. It's amazing how easily the only copy can get lost. Perhaps even hide a copy away in your files for future reference. If you are fortunate enough to have a runner helping with the setup, give him a copy to get started.

Once the control room is cleaned and ready, and all equipment is turned on and warming up, use the input/setup sheet to start setting up the studio. However, as session setup and protocol vary widely, it is not possible to detail every event you will encounter. This is a basic overview — there are many different instrument combinations and situations. Whatever works best for the musician is usually the right way. Different projects might:

- Record and keep all instruments during basics.

- Record one instrument at a time until the songs are complete.

- Record a full rhythm section, only to replace and/or repair all other instruments except the drums during overdubs. These other instruments might be played along only to help the drummer with the song structure, and to help him stay "in the groove." However, these other tracks, or sections of them, are often kept and used, as they may have a feel that gets lost during overdubs.

(AEH) ARTIST TUFF BEANS PRODUCER S. ARAGONES ENGINEER HERBIE HYNDE			DATE JULY 29 — STUDIO ☒A ☐B ☐C ASSISTANT A READER.		

INSTRUMENT	MICROPHONE	PARAMETER	INPUT	BUSS	OUTBOARD
BASS GUITAR AMP.	U·47 #1	CARDIOID	1	2	
BASS GUITAR · DIRECT	DI. BOX		2	3	
KICK DRUM	421		3	4	EQ→LIM 1
SNARE DRUM. TOP	SM 57		5	5	EQ 2
SNARE DRUM BOTTOM	451		6	5	EQ 3
HIGH HAT	451	-10db PAD	7	6	
TOM TOMS. LOW	421		8	7	
MID	421		9	7,8	
HIGH	421		10	8	
OVERHEAD RIDE	U·87	CARDIOID	11	9	
OVERHEAD CRASH 1	U·87	"	12	10	
OVERHEAD CRASH 2	U·87	"	13	9,10	
AMBIANCE 1 L	414	"	14	11	
AMBIANCE 1 R	414	"	15	12	
AMBIANCE 2 L	U·87	"	16	11	
AMBIANCE 2 R	U·87	"	17	12	
GUITAR 1 AMP	421		18	15	
GUITAR 1 DIRECT	DI. BOX		19	15	
GUITAR 2	SM·57	-10db PAD	20	16	
KEYBOARD 1 L ⟩MIDI	DIRECT		21	19	
" 1 R / TO,	"		22	20	
KEYBOARD 2 L / ✎	"		23	19	
" 2 R ⟩	"		24	20	
REFERENCE VOCAL	U·87		25		
TALK BACK			31	1	
CLICK			DIRECT	TO 23	
STEREO CUE 1 ⟶ GUITARS + KEYBOARDS					
STEREO CUE 2 ⟶ BASS GUITAR + DRUMS					
SEND 3 ⟶ ECHO CHAMBER 1 L		LINE IN 27			
R		LINE IN 28			

Figure 2.1. Input/Setup Sheet

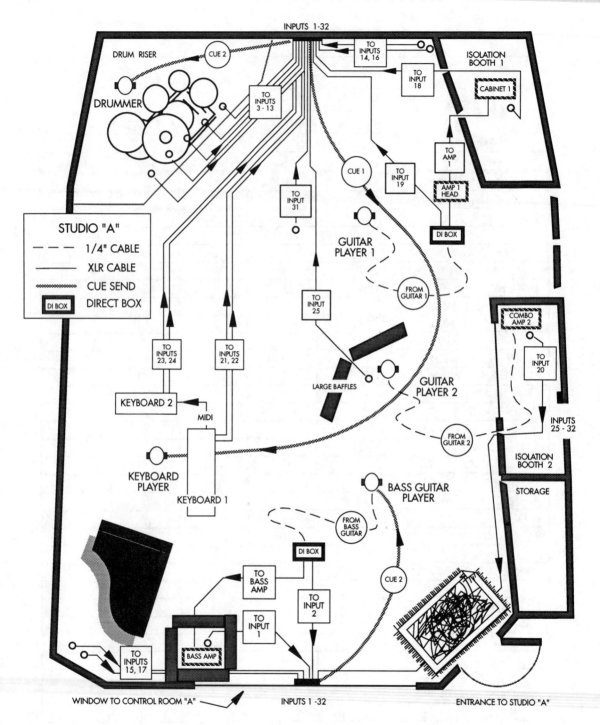

Figure 2.2. Back of Input/Setup Sheet

Any overdubs or repairs on these other tracks are usually recorded after the choice drum take is established. This choice take can be either one complete take or sections of different takes edited together. (A *take* in the studio usually refers to a performance recorded to tape. A *pass* usually refers to the tape passing the heads. Making a copy from one machine to another is called a pass, not a take.)

To be able to return to the same sounds to repair these tracks, sounds are written down using a setup sheet. (See Chapter Nine for more on setup sheets.) Of course, you can't really "write down a sound." This term refers to writing down the equipment and settings used in getting a particular sound.

- Program a computer to play all the parts at once.

- Simply set up all the instruments in the studio and play with no isolation or headphones, with amplifiers blaring, the way Elvis used to do it.

For overdubs, an input/setup sheet is not always necessary as the setup tends to be less involved than basics. It is not uncommon for the assistant to wait for the engineer to arrive before setting up for the overdub. Often the engineer does a monitor mix in the control room while the assistant sets up for the overdub in the studio. As well, setup and breakdown of equipment happens throughout the session, not just before the session, as with basics.

PLACING MUSICAL INSTRUMENTS

Some of the items in the studio that you don't regularly handle are the musical instruments. You set up the microphones, stands, cables, amplifiers and heads for the amplifiers. You may plug in the effects the musician will be using. You may even be required to go out to the amplifier and turn it up a notch, but the musicians will usually arrive with their instruments and set them up. You are only expected to haul the instruments in their cases to their correct location in the studio.

Don't handle or remove an instrument from its case without the owner's permission, and even then, care is of the utmost importance. Never play someone's instrument without first asking. If you do need to handle any of the musical instruments, keep in mind that a musician uses his instrument to make a living, like a carpenter uses a hammer, a doctor uses a scalpel, or a record producer uses a telephone. The tremendous amounts of time spent playing a beloved instrument may give the musician an unnatural bond with it.

ROAD CASES

Most larger musical instruments and equipment travel to and from recording studios in road cases. Figure 2.3. These are strong moveable boxes with wheels used to store, protect, and transport equipment. Road cases contain amplifiers, musical instruments, and accessories such as cables, tuners, strings, picks, keys, etc. When these cases arrive for the session, take them into the studio. If the studio is in use, put the road cases in a corner out of the way until the studio is available.

Figure 2.3. Road Case

Often road cases are stuffed full of equipment. Once the contents have been removed, this Pandora's box may be next to impossible to repack correctly without some sort of chart or list of contents. When unloading a road case filled with various kinds of equipment, make a list of everything removed, the order in which they came out, and maybe even a drawing of how everything was packed. The day will come toward the end of the project when everything that was in the road cases must be accounted for and repacked.

Store the empty road cases in an out-of-the-way place, such as a corner of the studio, or a separate storage area. If the cases stay in the studio, cover them with a packing blanket to prevent any buckles from rattling.

DRUMS

The heaviest and bulkiest of the instruments, such as the drums, amplifiers, and piano are placed first. Drums, like most instruments, should be left to the player or his roadie to assemble. Show him the correct placement, according to the setup sheet, and help haul the road cases into the studio. Setting the drums up correctly can be challenging for the assistant, as every drummer sets up his kit differently. In studios that own and use a certain set of drums, learn how to set those drums up properly. One day a drummer will arrive for the session with just his drumsticks, expecting to sit down and play.

Before starting the setup, find out if the engineer wants a carpet or large mat under the drum kit. It's far easier to lay out a carpet *before* the drums are in place. A sandbag, or something similarly heavy and stable may be placed in or in front of the kick drum to keep the kit from slowly sliding forward during the session.

Some drummers hit the drums hard enough to warrant taping the cymbal stands and snare drum stand to the floor to ensure they remain stationary throughout the session. Before doing anything this drastic, check with the engineer or musician after the kit is in place. If the pedals for the kick drum or high hat squeak, bring in some oil, and place it near the kit. Let the drummer or his drum technician oil the pedals.

Different songs may require different drum sounds, so a drummer will often have more than one of each drum with him. Keep these extra drums out of the way and covered. Drums with snares may buzz and rattle, and this sound can leak into the microphones. When snare drums are not in use, for instance overnight, remove the tension on the snares under the drum, but again, check with the drummer first. Once all the drums are in place, move on to the guitar amplifier setup.

AMPLIFIERS

Guitar amplifiers usually come in two different styles: combination (or combo amplifiers) and split amplifiers. Figure 2.4. Combo amplifiers house the amplification section and the speaker cabinet section in one unit. Split amplifiers are broken down into two separate sections:

1) The power section, also called the head (or top), where the volume and tone controls are located.

2) The cabinet section, also called the bottom, where the speakers are.

Figure 2.4. Split Amplifier and Combination Amplifier

These two sections are connected via heavy gauge speaker cable. The head can be stacked on top of the bottom cabinet for convenience, or the cabinet can be placed elsewhere. Placing the speaker cabinet from the rest of the studio isolates it, while the head stays with the musician. Separating the cabinet from the head also prevents the head from being damaged by cabinet vibrations.

During overdubs, the musician might be in the control room with the head, while the cabinet is out in the studio or in an isolation booth. Some musicians will stay next to the cabinet, as this is how they rehearse and perform. No matter where the musician is, he will probably need to reach the volume, tone, and standby controls (if he is unplugging to retune.)

Of course, different situations in the studio may require more than one cabinet or head, and in many different configurations. Sometimes one head feeds two speaker cabinets and each is recorded on separate tracks. The combinations are endless.

After finding out who will use which amplifier, wheel the road cases to the general areas where they will be placed, then remove the amplifier from the road case, and place it correctly. According to the input/setup sheet (fig. 2.1.), there are three amplifiers being used for this basic session :

Bass Amplifier

The bass guitar amplifier is baffled off to prevent the sound from leaking into other microphones in the rest of the studio, and to prevent the sound from the rest of the amplifiers from being picked up in the bass guitar amplifier microphone. (See later in this chapter for more on baffles.) The baffles are set up after the amplifiers are in place. If more isolation booths were available, the amplifier might be placed in one. It is very common to isolate amplifiers for recording. As the bass amplifier is being placed, leave enough space behind and beside it for the baffles. Then move on to the next setup.

Guitar 1 Amplifier

According to the input/setup sheet (fig. 2.1.), the amplifier used for guitar player 1 is split. The cabinet section is put in isolation booth 1, while the head stays with the musician in the studio. Put a small table near the musician to hold the head, along with any accessories for the guitar player.

Guitar 2 Amplifier

The amplifier used for guitar player 2 is not split, according to the input/setup sheet illustration, so assume it is a combo amp. This amplifier goes in isolation booth 2. At this point, just place the amplifiers, don't connect them.

Once all the amplifiers are placed, plug them into the nearest electrical power box. Always use the power cable that comes with the amplifier. Don't turn the amplifier on without the instrument connected to it. Better yet, let the musician turn his amplifier on. Place a table nearby for this guitar player as well.

KEYBOARDS

Piano

The piano is one of the first instruments to be positioned before the session, since it would be very difficult to maneuver it through a studio full of cables, microphone stands, and baffles. Most larger studios have at least one piano. The input/setup sheet (fig. 2.1.) states that the piano is not being used for this basic session, so move it into a corner out of the way. Cover it with blankets as the strings may ring out sympathetically during the session.

If the piano were being used, it would be placed for the session, and a piano tuner would come in before the session to tune it. It wouldn't be moved again, since moving a piano may throw it out of tune. Sometimes, after a piano is set up and the microphones are correctly placed, the piano is baffled off and covered with blankets for isolation. The piano player then stays in the studio with the rest of the musicians, with no worry of leakage to or from other microphones.

Occasionally clean the piano with a soft chamois and some furniture polish. Never dip it in soapy water and hose it down.

Organs

Some organs are quite bulky and require amplification, either from an internal speaker, or from an external Leslie. A Leslie is a speaker system much like a traditional guitar amplifier, only with rotating horn speakers inside. The speed of rotation is determined by the musician playing the instrument. A Leslie can be used to amplify any instrument, including a guitar. The cabinet is sometimes isolated, and recorded much like a guitar amplifier.

Electronic Keyboards

Because, according to the input/setup sheet (fig. 2.1.), the keyboards are MIDI'd to each other, place the master keyboard in a convenient location for the musician to play. (See Chapter Three for more on MIDI.) Most players will have enough stands to hold all their keyboards, but an extra stand, or even a small table may be needed for additional keyboards. Again, the musician usually sets up his own instrument. Some-times the electronic keyboards are played in the control room, as they normally use no amplification, just direct signal into the desk.

ADDITIONAL INSTRUMENTS

After all the larger instruments, amplifiers, and baffles are in place, bring in the remaining instruments, such as individual guitars, horns, etc. Place these instruments within easy reach of the musicians. Leave these instruments in their road cases, and let the musicians deal with them.

Often, a musician may have more than one instrument out and ready to be played. If an acoustic stringed instrument is set up and not being played during the recording, tell the engineer; he may want the musician to put it away, or cover it with a towel to prevent it from ringing out sympathetically. Perhaps cover acoustic instruments in the control room, as loud monitors may also cause the strings to ring out.

TUNERS

Tuners are essential for most stringed instruments in the studio unless either the musician has perfect pitch and does all the tuning by ear, or the music is more important than the tuning — like when Bob Dylan records. When I was assistant engineer on Bob Dylan's "Empire Burlesque" he asked me to tune his guitar before an overdub. (Yet another of the assistant's never-ending duties.) When I had tuned the E, B, and G strings, he took the guitar away saying he was only going to play those strings for the overdub.

Most musicians stay in tune throughout a session by using a consistently reliable tuner. There are presently three kinds of tuners:

1) A tuning fork. This is a U-shaped device with a metal handle that when struck, produces a fixed tone in perfect pitch, commonly A-440.

2) An electronic tuner. These are quite popular today because of their ease of use and reasonable cost. Electronic tuners usually have auto calibration, an internal tuning tone, a built-in microphone and a line input.

3) A strobe tuner. These use a revolving disc with various slots located at exact distances from each other. When the disc turns at certain speeds, the slots become a single line. Think of watching the spokes of a wagon wheel. As the wheel turns, the spokes or lines appear to be slowly revolving forward or backward. When the lines on the strobe appear stationary, the note is in tune.

A strobe tuner needs to be calibrated every time it is moved or turned on. Historically, a tuning fork has been used to calibrate a strobe tuner. If no tuning fork is available, send a continuous single tone to the tuner from either a variable oscillator, or send a pure A-440 tone from the output of a keyboard.

Once the tuner is calibrated, record a section of the calibration tone on one track of the multitrack tape, usually where the alignment tones are. Notice on the tape label (fig. 8.3.) it contains a 30 second tuning tone. This tone is used for the complete project as a source of reference to calibrate all tuners. Sometimes more than one tone is recorded to tape.

Access the input of the tuner with either a line input, or a microphone. Most strobe tuners come with a microphone, which is usually kept in a small slot in the back of the tuner. If using a line input to the tuner, the musician may need to unplug his instrument every time he needs to check his tuning.

Most tuners have an input and output, so the signal can go through the tuner before being recorded, allowing the tuner to continually stay active. However, many engineers do not want the extra processing of a tuner in the signal path being recorded. Often the musician simply unplugs the cable from the amplifier, and plugs into the input of the tuner. The engineer may choose to assign a buss on the instrument input channel from the desk directly to the input of the tuner. This avoids having the musician unplug every time he needs to check his tuning.

STUDIO EQUIPMENT SETUP

BAFFLES

For some recordings, such as basics, certain instruments might be isolated from the rest of the instruments to avoid unwanted leakage into other microphones. Most studios have at least one isolation booth, some studios have many. When all isolation booths are being used, or are inappropriate to use, baffles (sometimes called gobos) may be used. Figure 2.5. Baffles are heavy movable walls used to isolate a musician or instrument to prevent unwanted leakage to or from other microphones from within the studio. One side of the baffle is usually hard wood, for a more reflective sound, and the other side is cloth, for more absorbency. The engineer will decide which way he wants the baffles to face.

Baffles can be large enough to construct a small booth for a musician to stand in. Larger baffles may have windows in the top half, so an isolated musician can see the rest of the session.

Smaller baffles can be used to build an isolation booth for amplifiers, such as the setup for the bass guitar on the input/setup sheet. To isolate an amplifier, place the baffles around three sides of it. If the baffles have wheels, turn them over on their sides. The isolation is much better, and they won't roll away during the bass solo.

Figure 2.5. Baffles

Place another baffle on top of the three walls, making a roof. Figure 2.6. Leave the front baffle open for the musician and engineer to access the controls and microphone. Once the sound is set up and the microphone is in place, close the open side with another baffle and cover the booth with packing blankets to ensure isolation.

Baffles are used not only to totally isolate a sound, as with the bass guitar setup, but also to deaden certain areas of the studio. Sometimes baffles are placed behind a singer during an overdub to prevent the ambiance of the studio from being picked up in the vocal microphone.

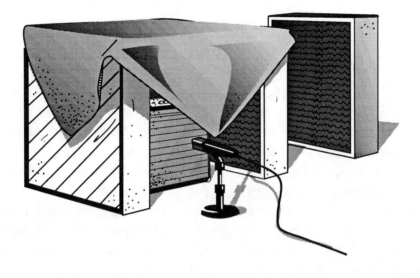

Figure 2.6. Baffles Creating An Isolation Booth

According to the input/setup sheet (fig. 2.1.), the large baffles being used for the singer won't totally isolate him. Although a small amount of leakage may be recorded, the singer — guitar player 2 as noted on the input/setup sheet — has freedom to walk around. The musicians' freedom to move about usually takes precedence over isolation. Often the band can be heard in the background on a vocal track recorded during basics. This vocal is referred to as the guide vocal, also called the live vocal.

Some studios have small movable isolation booths. These usually have no windows, can be placed anywhere in the studio, and can house an amplifier and its mic-rophones. Once the setup inside the booth is complete, the door is closed to isolate the contents totally from the rest of the studio. The musician, who is outside the booth with the rest of the musicians, can hear his amplifier only through his headphones.

Place the large baffles very early in the setup. Don't roll the baffles over cables, or between all the delicate musical instruments; baffles are usually large enough to be very awkward and unstable. Imagine the consequences of a 200-pound baffle falling over onto a carefully placed Stradivarius. A million-dollar antique would become a pile of very expensive toothpicks.

CHAIRS

When setting up for a larger session, chairs may be needed for the musicians. Placing chairs after the baffles have been set up allows you to see where all the musicians will be located, and where the microphone stands will be placed. As a rule of thumb, the larger the session, the earlier you set up the chairs. On most smaller sessions, a stack of chairs can be left in a corner, so if a musician needs one, he simply asks you, or grabs one for himself. However, for any session, large or small, if any musical instrument requires the musician to be seated, for example a cello, place the chair before the musician arrives. Once the chairs are in place, begin setting up the microphone stands.

MICROPHONE STANDS

Microphone stands are used to position microphones exactly where the engineer wants, and to ensure the microphones stay there for the duration of the recording. When setting up microphone stands:

- Always use stable, reliable, well balanced stands that will work with the instrument. All connections on the stands must be tight. If the connections on a stand won't grip, never use adhesive tape to hold the microphone at the correct height. Replace the stand. No matter how much tape is used, the weight of the microphone will eventually cause the grip to loosen. No one wants to watch a microphone slowly sink onto the strings of the piano during a fantastic take.

- Place the microphone stands throughout the studio according to the input/setup sheet, keeping in mind the instruments to be recorded. For example, if recording violins, you might place the microphones above the musicians. If recording French horns, you might place them behind the musicians.

- When setting up microphone stands in front of amplifiers, use a small stand with good maneuverability for exact microphone placement.

- Set all stands squarely on the floor, not resting on other stands. They must be solidly placed so they will not move.

- Don't try to connect a microphone to a stand that is in a difficult-to-reach position. Bring the microphone end of the boomstand to you, or you may risk dropping a sensitive microphone while leaning over to change it. If the microphone has already been exactly placed and you are changing it, try not to move the location of the stand. Find a good spot to make the change without being in a precarious position.

- While recording vocals or acoustic instruments, some engineers may want the microphone suspended from a boom, rather than resting on a stand. They may feel that the diaphragm within the microphone should hang, not rest on anything, as it does when the microphone sits upright.

- Always use matching stands and mounts when setting up stereo microphones, such as matched overhead microphones. Don't use one boom stand and one regular stand.

- When setting up boom stands, keep the counterweight end high enough to avoid someone accidentally hitting their head.

- Of course, don't place the drum stands before the drums are set up.

- When you are placing a microphone on a table, such as during an interview, use the smallest stand possible. Some microphones, such as lavalier, don't need a stand, as they are clipped directly on the lapel.

. . . .

Summary

Chapter Two explained what is involved in preparing the studio for a basic session:

- Stocking the control room and studio with all necessary stationery items used throughout the session.

- Understanding the input/setup sheet to set up the studio.

- Bringing in and placing all musical instruments and amplifiers.

- Correctly placing baffles, chairs and microphone stands.

CHAPTER THREE

· ·

Cables, Microphones And Headphones

When standing inside a nice clean modern recording studio, there is no indication that beneath the floor and behind the surrounding walls are miles of audio cables. These cables carry all signals throughout the studio and control room to the desk and patchbay. Most cables are permanently hard wired and usually only changed or accessed by qualified technical personnel. As these cables are not routinely accessed by the assistant engineer for setup of a session, this is not the time to discuss them. It's enough to know that the studio is connected to the desk via microphone input panels.

MICROPHONE INPUT PANELS

Microphone input panels are wall plates or movable boxes that connect the studio and control room to inputs and outputs of the desk. Figure 3.1. Most input panels are broken down into four sections:

1) XLR inputs. These allow input sources, such as microphones, to be connected directly to the desk from anywhere within the studio, isolation booths, and control room. The numbers on the input panels usually correspond with the inputs at the desk. For example, input 1 on the input panel is usually normalled to channel 1 on the desk. (See Chapter Six for more on normals.)

2) Cue send outputs. Signal also flows from the desk to outputs on the input panels in the studio. These outputs are used mainly for headphone cues.

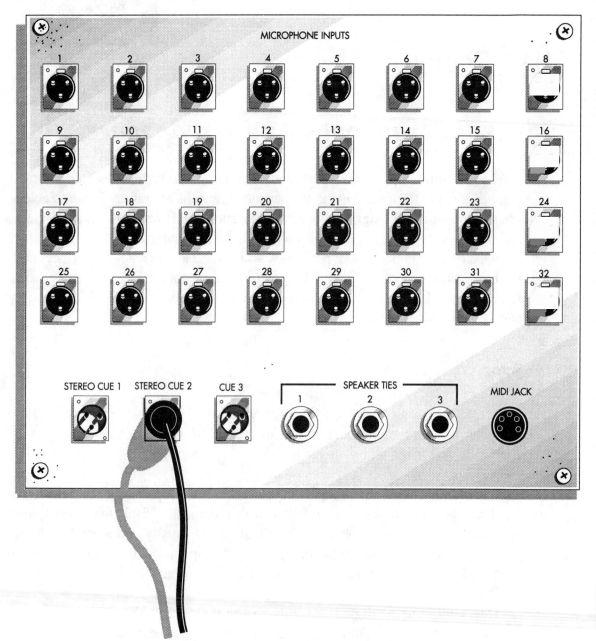

Figure 3.1. Microphone Input Panel

3) MIDI ports. Some input panels house MIDI ports for convenient connection of various MIDI equipment placed throughout the premises.

4) Speaker Ties. ¼" speaker ties are used mainly to connect amplifier heads to cabinets within the studio. This eliminates the need for long cables from going out through the control room door into the studio. Amplifier heads within the studio can also connect to cabinets elsewhere in the studio. For example, if the head is in one corner of the studio, and the cabinet is in an isolation booth across the room, they can be connected through the speaker ties on the input panels.

Most studios have at least two input panels in the studio, and often have smaller input panels in the isolation booths and the control room. Chances are slim that many instruments would be set up in an isolation booth and the control room, so there is usually no need for a full input panel.

Additional input panels in the control room connect the inputs and outputs of tape machines and outboard to the desk and patchbay. Some studios don't have these input panels, so the equipment is hard wired to the desk, limiting flexibility.

CABLES IN THE STUDIO

Although there are many different cable formats used in the recording studio, the main ones the assistant deals with daily are XLR (also called cannon), ¼", MIDI, and sometimes RCA cables. There are others, but these four tend to be handled most.

XLR CABLES

XLR cables are an industry standard. Most professional recording studio equipment is connected through XLR inputs and outputs. Figure 3.2. XLR cables are low impedance balanced lines used to carry a line or microphone level audio signal from microphone to desk, desk to multitrack machine, and sometimes even microphone directly to multitrack machine, plus many more combinations.

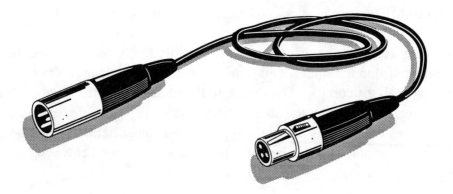

Figure 3.2. XLR Cable

Impedance is resistance, so low impedance cables can be extended for longer lengths without significant signal loss. As well, balanced cables are internally grounded, which eliminates inductance (signal transfer from neighboring cables.)

XLR cables consist of male connectors at one end, and female connectors at the other end. Signal usually flows in the direction of the pins. The standard flow of signal has the male sending the signal, and the female receiving it. A lot like dating.

¼" CABLES

¼" cables are high impedance, unbalanced lines, and are mainly used to run signal from instrument to amplifier. These cables are usually mono, but are available in stereo for equipment with stereo output jacks. Figure 3.3. Because ¼" cables are high impedance, they lose quality of signal with increased length, even as little as ten feet. Always use the thickest, most reliable ¼" cables available. Musicians often prefer to use their own ¼" cables.

¼" jacks are also used on speaker cable. However, speaker cable is heavy gauge cable used to carry power from amplifier to speaker. These are unshielded cables specifically designed to carry amplified signal, and should not be used to run signal from instrument to amplifier.

Figure 3.3. ¼" Cables, Stereo and Mono

MIDI CABLES

MIDI (Musical Instrument Digital Interface) cables are five-pin cables used to interface computers, keyboards, drum machines, samplers, and some outboard equipment. Data, including notes, length of notes, velocity, pitch change, modulation, attack, release, filters, and presets is sent through the MIDI cable from the master to the slaves. The slaves then duplicate the master, playing whatever it plays. Most newer keyboards and drum machines are completely integrated with MIDI, and are very easy to connect using MIDI cables. Figure 3.4. A healthy understanding of any and all MIDI equipment in your studio is highly recommended.

Figure 3.4. MIDI Cable

RCA CABLES

RCA cables are used on most home and semi-professional recording equipment, such as cassette machines. Figure 3.5. This equipment operates at a lower power level (-10dbv, unbalanced) than professional recording equipment (+4dbv, balanced.) This power level must be increased to conform with the desk's input level. A professional interface box may be used to bring the signal from -10dbv up to +4dbv. Once the signal is at the correct operating level, it can be properly integrated into the desk and the rest of the studio equipment through the patchbay.

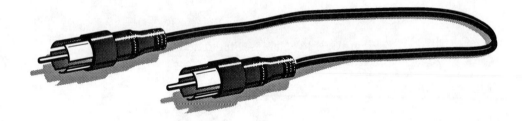

Figure 3.5. RCA Cable

POWER IN THE STUDIO

AC Cables

Of course, all equipment in the studio needs power. Whenever placing equipment, always use its original power cord. Perhaps even label the cord with the name and number of the corresponding equipment.

Often studios simply don't have enough outlets to house all the power cords from the various equipment in the studio. Quad boxes, or power strips, are heavy duty extension cords, often with four receptacles at one end, and a single plug at the other. With these strategically placed throughout the studio, most equipment will be close to an available power source.

If your studio has an iso grounded AC system — usually indicated by orange plugs in the wall, do not plug any recording equipment into regular white plugs.

Transformers

Guitar pedals, keyboards, and other recording equipment that operate on batteries will usually come with an AC transformer. Transformers step the power down from the wall outlet to a more acceptable voltage level. Figure 3.6.

Always use the transformer that comes with a piece of equipment, sometimes simply called the unit. If a unit's transformer is unavailable, check that the voltage and maximum current rating on the replacement transformer matches the recommended voltage and rating on the unit itself. The power level is labeled on both the transformer and the jack on the unit. Never use a transformer whose voltage doesn't correspond with that of the piece of equipment. As well, equipment that uses transformers might have a bad habit of humming, but there is not much you can do about this humming. Most other humming in the studio can be addressed.

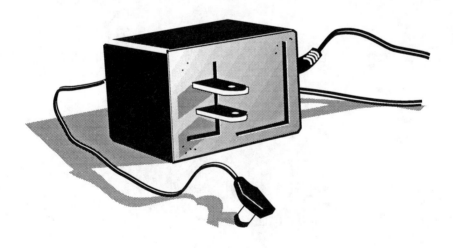

Figure 3.6. Power Transformer

Grounding

Ground loops occur when different circuits are grounded to different ground potentials, which may create a hum. For proper grounding, plug all equipment into the same circuit box, or ground potential. Sometimes simply flipping the ground switch on the direct box, or connecting the instrument or amplifier to a ground potential using an alligator clip will stop the hum. Single coil pickups on guitars may hum depending on where the musician is standing. The musician may have to turn and face a different direction to find the quietest spot. Fluorescent lights are notorious for creating a grounding hum. Some studios hum due to improper grounding.

As a last resort, isolate the grounding post on the plug with a ground lifter. Figure 3.7. This is an adapter that attaches to the power cord on the amplifier or other unit, and removes the grounding post. For optimum performance and minimal electric shock to the musician, properly ground every piece of equipment. Mind you, a guitarist might play one heck of a solo with 117 volts surging through his fingers.

Figure 3.7. Ground Lifter

Batteries

Many items such as direct boxes, guitar pedals and effects run on batteries, usually 9-volt. The studio should keep a supply of new batteries in the tech. shop. The number of batteries supplied by the studio may need to be written down on the work order, and charged to the client.

Whenever changing batteries, mark the date on the battery using a piece of adhesive tape. Then you, or whoever changes the battery, will know when it was last changed. If a 9-volt battery is not labeled, check its power level with a battery checker. Every studio should have a battery checker. Don't use the old trick of putting the battery on your tongue to check it. This is unreliable, and should really only be done when checking the battery in your car.

RUNNING CABLES ACCORDING TO THE INPUT/SETUP SHEET

GETTING CABLES

Now that all the baffles, chairs and microphone stands are set up, the cables need to be run. On larger sessions, lay out the cables before the microphones are placed. Because of the traffic and activity involved when running the cables, stands may get bumped or knocked over. This could damage a delicate microphone.

In some studios, standard practice is to bring out and run all the XLR cables, then all the ¼" cables, then finally all the AC power cables. In other studios, you set up the XLR cables, the ¼" cables, and the power cables for each instrument, then move on to the next instrument. The latter seems to work better as it lets a musician fine tune his sound while the rest of the studio is being set up. Before setting up the studio for a large session:

- Check that there are enough cables. This includes extension cords for electrical outlets, XLR cables, ¼" guitar cables and, if the situation calls for it, MIDI cables. If you are short on cables, arrange to get more, either from elsewhere on the premises, or from a neighboring studio. The session should never have to stop due to lack of functional cables.

• Although there may be enough cables, some may be questionable. Often the rarely used cables in the studio are the thin flimsy ones, the short ones, and the ones with exposed wires. Always use the thickest, most reliable cables available.

• When you must use the thin questionable cables, use them on non-input items, such as headphones. If something goes wrong with the cable, the musician will instantly notice, and it won't affect the actual recording. If a questionable cable is used on a microphone, its breakdown may not be noticed immediately.

• Many studios store cables according to length. Some studios have specific areas housing different lengths of cable, while some use colored tags for different lengths of cable. If your studio isn't using this kind of system, try to organize it.

• When selecting cables by length, keep in mind what they will be used for. If the microphone stands are close to the wall inputs, the longest cables won't be necessary. Use cables that are slightly longer than needed, as cables that are too short are easily tripped on. Never use a cable that is so short that it's taut. A musician tripping, falling, and breaking his neck is one thing, but think of the damage to the microphone and input panel. Better to extend it or exchange it for a longer cable than risk this kind of damage.

• The possibility of a musician moving into the control room should be taken into account when setting up. Try to run the cables so it is easy for a musician to simply walk into the control room from the studio, instrument in hand, and continue recording without any change in sound. (See Chapter Nine for more on the musician moving from the studio to the control room.)

• When bringing out cables, keep the studio's cables and the musician's cables separate. When a musician has his own ¼" cables, use them, but label them to make sure they don't get mixed up with the studio's cables. The musician should leave with everything he arrived with, except perhaps, his sanity.

• Bring out all the cables, and even a few extra so you won't have to go hunting around when you need them. Untie any knots in them, and place all the microphone cables on the floor near the input panels.

CONNECTIONS AND PLACEMENT

Now that all cables are in the studio, run them as described on the input/setup sheet (fig. 2.1.). Notice how all the instruments are laid out, with the drums in one section, the guitars in another, the keyboards in another. This is so the individual instruments are organized at the desk. Sometimes the engineer might skip an input, such as on a drum setup, in case an additional drum microphone needs to be introduced. This avoids a lone drum input coming in at the other end of the desk.

Again, as all recording sessions differ, there are many ways to set up the equipment. The following setup is included only as a reference:

1) According to the input/setup sheet (fig. 2.1.), the bass guitar setup has two inputs. One is a microphone in front of the amplifier, and the other is a direct signal from the bass guitar into the desk. Get the first XLR cable and remove the cable tie. (A cable tie is a small piece of plastic or Velcro used to keep a cable properly wrapped when stored.) Often a cable tie is permanently fastened to one end of the XLR cable so it's always there when needed.

2) Grasp the cable's male end, and connect it to input 1 on the input panel. If the studio has more than one input panel, use the one closest to the instrument.

3) The connectors, or jacks, have locks that keep them attached while plugged in. This lock will click when the cables are correctly connected. After the click, gently tug on the cable to see if it is locked. If you don't hear a click when plugging in a cable, remove it from the input and try again.

4) With the remainder of the cable in your hand, walk over to the correct microphone stand, unraveling the cable as you go. When wrapped correctly, the cable should unravel with nary a knot or tangle. (See Chapter Twelve for more on wrapping cables.)

5) Leave the rest of the cable at the base of the microphone stand. If the stand needs to be moved, extra cable is at the base of the stand, not back at the wall. Hang the female end of the cable over its respective microphone stand. This leaves no doubt which cable connects to which microphone. Move on to the next cable.

6) According to the input/setup sheet, input 2 is not a microphone, but the output of a direct box. Put the direct box on the floor close to where the musician will be. Run the next XLR cable from the XLR output of the direct box to input 2, again leaving the excess cable on the floor near the direct box. (See later in this chapter for more on direct boxes.)

7) Connect one end of a ¼" cable to the input of the direct box and leave the other end loose for the musician to connect his instrument. A musician may prefer to use his own ¼" cable.

8) Run a second ¼" cable from the high impedance output of the direct box to the input of the amplifier. Again, keep the length of ¼" cables at a minimum.

9) Connect the power cable from the amplifier to an AC outlet. Keep audio cables and electrical cables from running parallel, as this may introduce AC hum (60/50 hz.) into your low level audio signal. If theses cables must cross, keep them at right angles.

10) Leave the power on the amplifier off. If the amplifier is turned on without the instrument connected, the power may load down and blow a fuse.

11) The bass guitar setup is now complete, except for the microphone, which you will bring in after all cables are run. When the musician arrives, he can plug in the instrument, turn on the amplifier and begin warming up. The next instrument on the input/setup sheet is the drums.

12) The drum microphones get plugged into inputs 3 to 17, leaving input 4 open. Run the XLR cables as described earlier. Watch that no two cables get accidentally plugged into the same input at different input panels.

13) Don't wrap the cables all neatly in a row across the floor — they can get very tangled, making them difficult to trace. Keep them somewhat neat, but not sprawled out across the floor.

14) Don't tape cables to the floor. They become difficult to move or change in a hurry, plus tape leaves a residual sticky film on the cable and floor. In the control room and busier areas, such as doorways, put a small rug over the cables. This keeps them in place and stops anyone from tripping on them. Next on the input/setup sheet are the microphone cables for the other guitar amplifiers.

15) The setup for guitar 1 has the head of the amplifier with the musician in the studio, and the bottom of the amplifier, or speaker cabinet, in isolation booth 1. According to the input/setup sheet, this guitar setup also uses a direct box.

16) Connect the cables as you did for the bass guitar, with an XLR cable going to input 18 from the microphone stand in isolation booth 1. Then run another XLR cable going to input 19 from the direct box.

17) Again, connect one end of a ¼" cable to the input to the direct box, and leave the other end loose for the musician to connect his instrument. Run a second ¼" cable from the high impedance output of the direct box into the input of the amplifier. Connect the power cables for the amplifier.

18) The setup for guitar 2, a combo amplifier, is in isolation booth 2. As there is no direct signal on this setup, no direct box is needed. Run a single cable to input 20 from the microphone stand in the isolation booth.

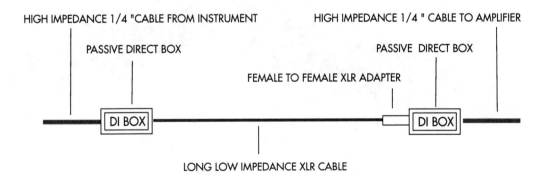

Figure 3.8. High Impedance Cable Extension

19) To get signal from guitar 2 all the way to the amplifier in isolation booth 1, one method is to run a long unbalanced ¼" cable. Because unbalanced high impedance lines lose signal with increased length, you might consider another option. Get two passive direct boxes, two ¼" cables, one long XLR cable, and a "same sex" female to female XLR adapter. Plug one of the ¼" cables from the instrument into a direct box, changing the impedance of the signal from high to low. (If necessary, the "send" direct box can be either active or passive.) Then run a low impedance (XLR) cable from the first direct box into the isolation booth, and into another passive direct box, using the female to female adapter. This then changes the signal back to high impedance. Come out of the ¼" output of the direct box, and into the input of the amplifier. Figure 3.8. This combination will sound better than one long ¼" guitar style cable.

20) Notice on the input/setup sheet (fig. 2.1.), input 20 needs a -10db in-line microphone pad. Figure 3.9. Because the microphone being used lacks an internal pad, place an in-line pad between the microphone and the cable to reduce signal gain. However, in-line pads will interfere with a condenser microphone's phantom power. (See Chapter Six for more on phantom power.) The "Shure SM-57" used on this amplifier is not a condenser microphone, but a dynamic microphone. Next is on the input/setup sheet are the keyboards.

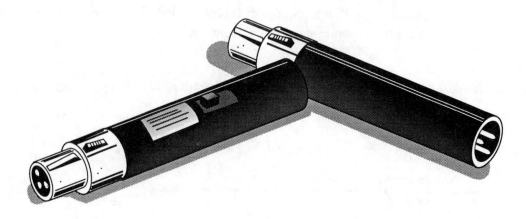

Figure 3.9. In-Line Microphone Pad

21) Some keyboards have both high and low impedance jacks on the back panel. High impedance (¼") output levels might need to be changed to a more acceptable level using direct boxes. To save time, and to save direct boxes for other instruments, use the keyboards low impedance (XLR) output jacks.

22) If the keyboards are being recorded in stereo, label both ends of the cables and, if used, label both direct boxes as left and right. Any signal flow problems encountered can then be easily traced.

23) According to the input/setup sheet (fig. 2.1.), keyboard 1 is connected to inputs 21 and 22, and keyboard 2 is connected to inputs 23 and 24. Because the keyboards do not use microphones, cables can be run from the output of the keyboards directly to the input panel.

24) Most keyboards don't use external amplifiers, therefore they can be plugged in and turned on without fear of blowing fuses.

25) After the keyboards are connected to the input panels, MIDI them together. According to the input/setup sheet, the master, which is keyboard 1, is MIDI'd to the slave, which is keyboard 2. Connect a MIDI cable from MIDI output on the master keyboard into MIDI input on the slave keyboard.

Programmed MIDI instruments, such as drum machines, often stay in the control room, and are connected to the desk via input panels in the control room. Once all the keyboards are set up, all that is left is the vocal microphone and the talkback microphone.

26) A guide vocal track is often recorded with a basic track. This helps everyone in the studio and control room know where they are within the structure of the song at any given time, plus it keeps the flow of the song consistent. Often the guide vocal is used in part or in whole for the final vocal. The final vocal is the choice vocal track that ends up on the final mixdown.

There tends to be a certain magic that occurs when everyone is playing together in the studio. When a singer is doing an overdub alone in the studio without the rest of the band, the music in the headphones may not elicit such an inspired performance. Looking at the input/setup sheet, guitar player 2 will be singing the guide vocals.

27) Run the cable for the guide vocal microphone from the vocal microphone stand to input 25.

28) The only cable left to be set up is for the talkback microphone. This is a centrally located microphone, used during larger sessions for the musicians to talk to the people in the control room, and to each other. Often the rest of the microphones in the studio are off axis with the musicians, so when they are talking with the people in the control room, or even with each other, no microphone picks what they are saying.

Run this cable from the microphone stand to input 31, again according to the input/setup sheet (fig. 2.1.). Once all cables and inputs for the session are connected, move on to the direct boxes and effects boxes.

DIRECT INPUT BOXES

The direct output level from electric instruments, such as guitars, some keyboards, and pickups from acoustic instruments is not compatible with the input to the professional recording desk. This signal must be altered by using a direct input box. The direct input box, usually called a DI, or direct box, converts signal from the high impedance output (¼") of the instrument to match the low impedance input (XLR) of the desk. Figure 3.10. The box also has a ¼" output for signal to continue, often to an amplifier, allowing the signal to go to both the desk and the amplifier.

Direct boxes are either active or passive. Active boxes convert impedance one way, from high to low. Passive boxes, by nature of the transformer in them, can convert impedance both ways, high to low, and low to high.

Direct boxes may be used, among other applications, to send a low impedance signal from the desk to a high impedance input of a guitar amplifier. This is sometimes done to add the sound of an amplifier to previously recorded tracks. Active direct boxes need power, either AC or batteries. If batteries are used, unplug cables into direct boxes during long periods of inactivity, such as overnight, to eliminate power drain on the batteries.

Direct boxes also have a ground reverse switch, used to stop electrical hums and buzzes. Most also have a pad switch, and some have a trim pot to set an exact operating level.

EFFECTS BOXES

The musician may want to insert additional signal processing devices into the signal before it is sent to the desk, such as distortion pedals, additional equalization, fuzz, wah-wah etc. To do this, short ¼" cables are needed to connect them. He will also need either additional power strips, or more batteries.

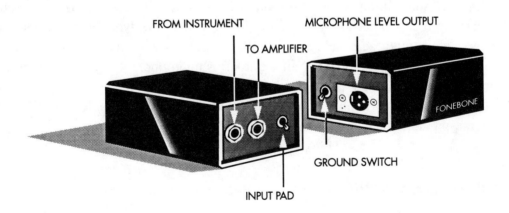

Figure 3.10. Direct Box

MICROPHONES

Microphone care is a vastly important matter. Poorly maintained microphones simply will not endure as well as those properly looked after. While most equipment in the studio is sturdy enough to withstand the occasional mishandling, only the most durable microphones can weather such treatment. Many of the best and most popular microphones used in the studio today are decades old — proof that proper care and handling can yield quality long term results.

Think of yourself as the engineer. Would you prefer old scratched and dented microphones that look as if they had been tossed around, or would you prefer pristine, well taken care of microphones? The answer seems obvious.

The setting of parameters on most microphones is basic, yet each microphone is different. Some microphones have no changeable parameters, while others have switches on the outer casing. Some microphones have changeable heads for different pads (used to lower the input level), different roll-offs (filters used to remove very low or high frequencies), and different polar patterns (grid patterns of a microphones response field, such as cardioid, omni-directional, bi-directional, or uni-directional.) Contrary to popular belief, a polar pattern is not a weather front from Alaska.

Engineers unfamiliar with all of your studio's microphones will ask for details regarding their operation. You should know which are dynamic, condenser, or ribbon, along with each one's pad, roll off, and polar pattern options. You also need to know the make and model of all the studio's microphones, how many there are, and each microphone's primary application. Whenever the engineer's choice of microphones isn't available, you should be able to choose a suitable substitute, and tell the engineer when he arrives.

GETTING MICROPHONES

The microphone room is the home for all the microphones. Some studios keep the microphones in their original boxes, but realistically, after years of use these boxes get misplaced, lost, or discarded. Often studios store microphones on padded shelves in a dry cool room to keep them well protected.

The rest of the microphone supplies, such as microphone pads, clamps, shock mounts, windscreens, power supplies, and everything else associated with microphones are also stored here. When bringing in the microphones:

- Carry one in each hand, even if many trips are necessary. Set up the microphones on one instrument at a time.

- Lay them out on a blanket on the floor or a table. Avoid putting microphones directly on the floor as they attract moisture and dust, and are easily stepped on or kicked about.

- Never put a tube microphone on a floor or table. Bring it out and immediately place it on the microphone stand. Tube microphones are too expensive and fragile to be placed anywhere but in their case, or on a microphone stand. Bring out the tube microphone's external power supply, and place it near the input panel. When the setup is complete, turn the power supply on, as a tube microphone needs at least 30 minutes to warm up. Leave the power supply on for the rest of the session.

- Never put microphones on a bare piano as they may scratch the surface or worse, roll off and fall onto the floor. This gives a new meaning to the term, "microphone roll-off."

CONNECTION MOUNTS

Microphones use two different kinds of mounts. One is the standard clip, also called a clutch, which grips the microphone to hold it in place. The other mount uses a rubber or foam casing to isolate any vibrations from the stand and floor. When getting the connection mounts, keep the following in mind;

- When recording in stereo, use the same type of mount for both microphones. Don't put a shock mount on one, and a regular clip on the other.

• Although mounts tend to get lost and broken, never use adhesive tape to modify microphones and mounts. Arrange to get the correct mounts. With adhesive tape, the grip will loosen and the microphone may drop to the floor. When mounts are always kept with their microphones, they are less likely to get lost.

• Quick-lock connectors are spring loaded locks used to connect and disconnect microphones quickly and easily from their stands. Figure 3.11. Without a quick-lock, the microphone must be screwed and unscrewed to the stand every time it is used. To do this, grasp the microphone and screw the stand to the microphone, rather than screwing the microphone to the stand. The other option is to remove the microphone from the mount, screw the mount on to the stand, and then re-connect the microphone to the mount.

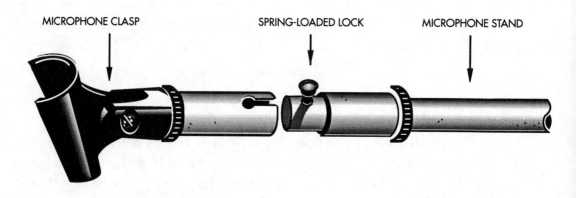

MICROPHONE CLASP   SPRING-LOADED LOCK   MICROPHONE STAND

Figure 3.11. Quick-Lock Connectors

MICROPHONE PLACEMENT

1) Starting with the bass guitar setup, bring out the microphone as described on the input/setup sheet (fig. 2.1.).

2) The bass guitar amplifier will be recorded with a Neumann U-47 tube microphone. Notice the engineer wants Neumann U-47 #2. Some studios label their microphones of the same make and model, such as U-47 #1, #2, and #3, etc.

   As individual microphones of the same make and model may each have slightly different characteristics, the engineer may request a specific microphone for vocals or for certain sensitive instruments. After working with all the studio's microphones, a good engineer will be able to hear slight differences in sound from one identical make and model to another.

3) Before placing the microphone in front of the bass amplifier, set any pads, roll-offs, or polar patterns according to the input/setup sheet. Setting the parameters is far easier when the microphone is still in your hand.

4) Connect the microphone to the stand that was previously placed, making sure the active side of the microphone is aiming toward the amplifier. Connect the cable resting on the stand to the microphone. The microphone is now connected to input 1.

5) As the bass guitar setup uses one microphone and one direct line, move on to setting up the microphones for the next instrument on the input/setup sheet — the drums.

6) Bring out and fasten all the drum microphones to their stands. Always double check that each microphone is firmly connected to the stand before moving on. If a microphone drops off a stand during the session, everyone turns and looks at the assistant.

7) According to the input/setup sheet, two stereo pairs of microphones, inputs 14-17, are set up in opposite corners of the studio to record the ambiance of the drum kit. For this setup all amplifiers are isolated, so the only sound in the studio is the sound of the drums.

Engineers sometimes like to record not only the close microphones on the drums, but distant microphones in the studio as well. This creates a certain ambient depth that simply cannot be re-created electronically. Engineers often want to try various microphone combinations to hear which ones sound best for different applications. They will choose the best ones and disregard the others. In this example, only one pair of ambient microphones would be used. Next on the input/setup sheet are the guitar amplifiers.

8) Place a Sennheiser 421 in front of the speaker cabinet in isolation booth 1, and a Shure SM-57 in front of the guitar amplifier in isolation booth 2. This is a common setup for guitars.

9) Run a ¼" speaker cable from the head in the studio, where the musician is located, to the speaker cabinet in isolation booth 1. This cable will usually come with the amplifier. After this setup, move on to the next item, the keyboards.

10) The keyboards need no microphones.

11) The vocal microphone uses a Neumann U-87, with a cardioid polar pattern.

12) Notice on the input/setup sheet that the only requirement for the talkback microphone is that it should be omni-directional. As most of the best microphones are probably already being used for the setup, use your judgment and set up whatever microphone is left. An omni-directional pattern is needed to capture the whole studio.

The engineer will often record talkback microphones during the session. In this example, notice the talkback microphone is bussed to track 1.

13) When the engineer arrives for the session, he will come out and place all the microphones precisely.

POP FILTERS

Many studios use a nylon pop filter, also called a windscreen, placed in front of a vocal microphone to keep any wind, or pop sounds from being recorded. Windscreens are quite popular because they are easy to make, easy to set up, and very effective.

A few studios use a nylon stocking wrapped around a bent wire coat hanger, and taped to a microphone stand. Figure 3.12. This looks very unprofessional, so replace this with a crochet hoop, a fresh nylon stocking, and a proper connection. When putting the windscreen in front of the microphone, give it its own stand, unless there is a housing to hold it in place.

The old foam windscreens, or pop filters, are certainly still used. Note that on some pop filters there is a small hole in front. This hole is to be placed over the polar pattern indicator to see the polar pattern or pad without moving the pop filter.

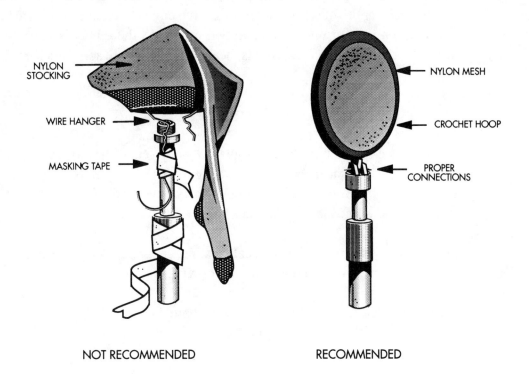

Figure 3.12. Pop Filters

ROOM MICROPHONES

Most studios have a room microphone that is permanently mounted somewhere within the studio, and accessible at the patchbay. The people in the control room can always hear what is happening in the studio, even if no microphones are apparent. Avoid voicing your dissatisfaction with the studio owner. He may be listening.

HEADPHONES

Headphones are used for isolation, letting the listener hear any instrument at any level. During basics, musicians will want different mixes in their headphones, so the engineer sets up as many cue mixes (also called the headphone mixes) as needed. During overdubs, a musician needs to hear himself and the previously recorded program through the headphones. Most studios have at least two cue outputs on each input panel. This leaves many options for the engineer. Because the signal can be split with headphone boxes, the engineer can send two stereo mixes, four mono mixes, or one stereo and two mono. As there may be more musicians than cue outputs on the input panels, headphone boxes are sometimes used.

HEADPHONE BOXES

Headphone boxes split the cue signal to many sets of headphones, letting more than one musician hear the same mix. Figure 3.13. is a breakdown of a standard head-phone box. Some headphone boxes may have fewer features than this, some may have more. Most boxes include:

1) An input, used to receive a signal from the cue send. This is the main input into the headphone box, and is either ¼" or XLR.

2) Volume controls. Pretty obvious what these do.

3) Stereo/mono switches. If additional cue sends are needed, there may be no other option than to use mono sends. To do this, the engineer might set up two separate mono cues from the left and right side of a stereo send. When the switch on the headphone box is on 1, the left side of the stereo cue is sending a mono signal to the headphones. When the switch is on 2, the right side of the stereo cue is sending a different mono signal to the headphones.

4) Individual headphone outputs, either ¼" or XLR. During large sessions, more than one set of headphones can be connected to one box.

5) A through output by which an unaltered signal can be sent to additional headphone boxes in the studio.

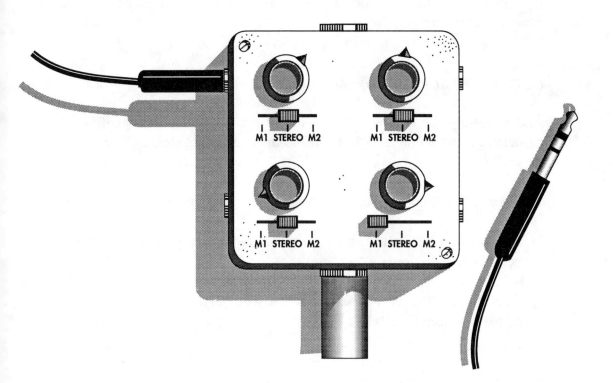

Figure 3.13. Headphone Box

Cue Options

There are many ways to send signal to the musicians' headphones. Musicians often need their own headphone mix to hear exactly the right combination of instruments. When everyone shares one cue mix, each person invariably wants himself a little louder than everyone else.

Some studios even have mini mixers for cue, so each musician has control over the level of each channel. If he wants to be louder in the headphone mix, he simply reaches over and turns himself up. More common is the engineer doing a headphone mix at the desk.

According to the input/setup sheet (fig. 2.1.), the drummer and bass player get one cue mix, and the rest of the musicians get another. Cue send 1 on the input panel feeds headphone boxes for the drummer and bass player. Cue send 2 on the input panel feeds the rest of the musicians. These cue sends might be normalled to mono or stereo sends on the desk.

GETTING HEADPHONES/PLACEMENT

After getting the correct setup from the input/setup sheet regarding which musician gets what cue send, bring the headphones, the cables, and the boxes into the studio.

1) Place the headphones throughout the studio where they will be used.

2) Run the cables from the correct cue send output on the input panel into the headphone box.

3) Leave the excess cable on the floor next to the headphone box in case it needs to be moved. Keep the box and cable out of the way, leaving the musician enough room to move around.

4) Before plugging any headphones, check that the cue amplifiers are on.

5) Connect the headphones, checking that everyone gets their proper cue send, and all headphones are working.

6) Set the headphones on a music stand, or a chair, not over the microphone stand, where they may feed back through the microphone.

7) Keep a spare set of headphones and a headphone box set up off to one side. Sometimes headphones will work during setup, but will break down during the session. Having an extra setup ready will save time.

8) Some musicians prefer certain models of headphones. Once a musician is happy with his setup, stay with that setup. Use the same model headphones and box for him for the duration of the project.

Headphones For The Engineer

Keep a set of headphones and a headphone box near the desk for the engineer to use when setting up cue mixes. He will not want his headphones as loud as the musicians have theirs, so turn his headphone box down and unplug the headphones. Even the lowest of level coming out of a headphone in the control room can throw the engineer. He will plug them in when he needs to check the cue mixes.

Some desks have a headphone output, but this is only useful if the engineer wants to hear the main monitor mix, not the individual headphone mixes. Don't put the engineer's headphones too close to the talkback microphone as they might feed back when he presses the talkback button.

Headphones For The Assistant

You will also need a set of headphones with a long cord, not necessarily to hear the cue mixes, but to find sections of tape, trim samples, set delay times, check returns, or to change settings on equipment.

As well, when the musicians see you wearing headphones, they think you are really getting into their music. With creative patching and headphones, you can do everything in relative silence while the rest of the room remains undisturbed.

To set up the headphones:

1) Patch from the output of the unit being checked, into the input of a nearby cassette machine.

2) Put the cassette machine in *record pause* and monitor through the headphones.

3) Whenever you wear headphones, keep the volume down. Headphones can pump a lot of air pressure, which can be quite damaging to the eardrums.

   Some musicians love to have the headphones obscenely loud, because of the impact. Think of the impact of being hit by a bus because you were too deaf to hear the driver honking the horn at you.

. . . .

Summary

Chapter Three explained how to retrieve and place all cables, microphones and headphones for a session:

• The most common cables used in the studio, and their connection to the input panels.

• Different power sources for different applications.

• Using the input/setup sheet to correctly retrieve and place all microphones on their proper stands and connection mounts.

• Connecting the cables to the microphones, proper placement of microphones and pop filters.

• Laying out all headphones and headphone boxes for the musicians and the engineer.

CHAPTER FOUR

. . . .

Tapes and Machines

The recording machines covered in this section include both analog and digital formats. While many studios today still rely on analog tape multitrack recording, decreasing prices of new technologies are allowing more and more studios to get into digital formats.

Some engineers prefer analog recording, some prefer digital recording, and some prefer various combinations of both. Both analog and digital formats are widely accepted, and each can deliver high-quality results. Whatever format the engineer will be using, make sure you understand the operation and parameters of the machines.

MACHINE PLACEMENT

Before you check the machine alignment, the machine must first be in the right spot. Many recording studios have one large machine room, with each control room off it, allowing each control room access to all available machines.

If the engineer can't see the meters because of the placement of the multitrack machines, tell the manager or the technical department. A more suitable location may need to be found. However, moving analog machines any distance may slightly change the alignment. Check the bias and alignment after such a move. (See later in this chapter for more on the alignment procedures.)

SETUP

Back of the Machine

All multitrack machines have an input and output audio section, usually accessed from the back of the unit. This is where the individual tracks receive and send signal. (The term "track" refers to the multitrack machine or tape, and the term "channel" refers the modules on the desk. For example, the multitrack machine has 24 tracks, and the desk has 56 channels.)

Many machines also have non-audio ports, including connection to external transport, timecode and video sync tracks, track remotes, and auto-locator remotes. Most machines have many cables hanging off the back, so recording studios often use DL, or EDAC multipair connectors, which connect the desk to the machine via a single port that houses all inputs and outputs. You must understand the function of each cable connected to the machine. Again, this is not the time to explain all technicalities of the recording studio.

Sometimes you might need to connect and disconnect cables at the back of the machine. The engineer may want the output of one track patched directly into a piece of outboard, or he may want to go directly into a track, bypassing the desk. If any cable to or from the machine gets changed during your session, label it with a piece if adhesive tape, stating its original routing. Of course, remove the tape after the cable is correctly returned. If these changes need to stay for the next session, leave a note for the assistant on that session explaining exactly what was changed, and why.

Front of the Machine

You must completely understand the heads and their functions, the transport section, the meters and all parameter settings. If something is improperly set up at the front of the machine, such as the VSO being on, the whole session may go by without it being noticed. When the problem is finally noticed, the damage may already be done. (See Chapter Ten for more on the variable speed oscillator.)

If you are unfamiliar with anything on the front of the machine, ask someone who knows. Of course, wait for an appropriate time to ask. When the engineer is deep in concentration during a difficult session, don't jump in and say "Geez, I wonder what happens if I press this itty bitty button here?"

Do not press a button, flip a switch, pull a cable, or turn a knob on any machine while the transport is in motion. If you do not know what something does, leave it alone. Learn the equipment through daily use, lots of reading, questioning engineers, and sneaking into the studio at 3 A.M.

CLEANING

During daily use, tape machines tend to get covered in pencil marks, grease smudges, pieces of tape, dust, and general studio grime, so the machines occasionally need cleaning. This will not involve any drastic measures, so power hoses and rubber boots will not be necessary. A simple pencil eraser will remove most of the marks, but sometimes a tissue with alcohol is needed. To remove small pieces of splicing tape from the chassis, cautious use of a razor blade may be in order. Be very careful to avoid scratching the machine. For best results:

- Always clean the heads before a session. Dip one or two cotton swabs into a bottle of isopropyl alcohol — never rubbing alcohol. Shake off the excess alcohol, then run the swab over the non-rubber surfaces of the tape path, starting with the heads. Start at one edge and swipe the swab over the head a few times to clean the full area of the head. Do this gently to avoid damaging the head. Remember, clean your head, don't scratch it.

- Clean the rubber rollers along the tape path with cotton swabs dipped in soapy water (not alcohol, which dries out rubber.)

- As tape machines run continually during a session, the oxide from the analog tape sheds onto the heads and rollers. This residue needs to be cleaned regularly, approximately every six hours. Do this during the session when the machine won't be in use for a few moments, whether you are asked to or not.

- Wait until the machine will not be in use for a few minutes. Remove the head protector, then unwind the tape from the front of the heads, keeping the tape well away from any stray droplets of alcohol.

- When the alcohol has evaporated, tighten the tape on both spindles, close the head protector, and press the *stop* button to activate the machine's mechanics.

DEMAGNETIZING

The heads and rollers along the analog tape path periodically become magnetized from being in constant contact with the tape, and need to be demagnetized with a demagnetizer (also called a de-magger.) Once before the session is enough. Turn off the multitrack machine before demagnetizing. To demagnetize the heads:

1) Remove all tapes from the vicinity — imagine what a device called a demagnetizer could do to an audio tape!

2) Turn on the de-magnetizer and hold it at least three feet (one meter) away from the heads.

3) Slowly bring it in and run it up and down the heads, not quite touching. Go over the heads two or three times, then demagnetize the non-rubber rollers, capstans, and all contact points along the tape path that may retain magnetism.

4) Slowly bring it away from the heads until it is again about one meter away. Turn the demagnetizer off and put it away.

Check that all the cables are properly connected, the machine parameters are correct, and the master gain on the desk is muted. Then turn on the machine. Report any meters that have burned out lights, or are not correctly reacting. As well, note any lights on the desk that are burnt out. Let the machine warm up for at least 30 minutes before checking the alignment. Check all tape machines for correct alignment before each session, and align if necessary.

TAPE RETRIEVAL

Tapes are made at the factory in batches, like cookies. Each unrecorded reel, called a virgin tape, has a sticker at the head of the reel that states its batch number. Before bringing these multitrack tapes to the control room, check the individual batch numbers for consistency. While most reels of analog tape will be fine, occasionally a bad reel or batch pops up. For consistency of sound quality, try to stay within a batch throughout the project. Of course, this isn't an issue if the project is small, and only one tape is being used. When retrieving the tapes:

- Bring enough virgin multitrack tape, mixdown tape, cassettes, DATs, and any other tape formats used for your session from the vault to the control room, and place them near their respective machines.

- When you must bring more than a few reels, use a small cart to transport them. Multitrack tapes are heavy, and lugging them to the control room every day may be counter-productive to your project, as well as to your back.

- If making more than one trip, bring up the alignment tape, or project tone reel with the first load. Hopefully someone from the technical staff will begin the alignment while you, or better yet, a runner schlep the rest of the tapes into the control room.

- Set the multitrack tapes on the floor near the multitrack machine, not stacked, but leaning against each other, like books in the library.

Keep in mind that these are the client's tapes, and must be handled in a completely professional manner. They must be neatly labeled, well organized and together. If the client sees his tapes mishandled, he loses confidence in you. So please, no cheeseburgers on the tape box.

HEADS, TAILS AND PRE-PRINT THROUGH

Now that all tapes are in the control room, start by loading the machine with the alignment reel. It, like all analog tapes in the studio, is stored tails out. Digital tapes are not susceptible to pre-print through so, as a rule, they are stored heads out.

When an analog tape is packed heads out on a reel, pre-print through may occur. This happens when recorded signal transfers from one layer of tape on a reel to an adjacent layer. When tapes are stored heads out, print through may be heard before a song starts. When tapes are stored tails out, print through would not occur until after the song starts, so it wouldn't normally be heard. Listen to the quiet part during the middle section of "Whole Lotta Love" by Led Zeppelin for a fine example of pre-print through.

ALIGNMENTS

There is an industry-wide standard for aligning tape machines. A tape recorded at one studio can be taken to another studio, and the record and playback levels should be comparable. Professional analog tape recorders are aligned to adjust for correct level and flattest frequency response during recording and playback. Once the machine is aligned for a specific project, reference tones are recorded, usually on reel 1 or the designated tone reel. These tones are then used for alignments during the rest of the project.

In larger studios, the technical staff is responsible for machine alignments. In smaller studios, the assistant is responsible for machine alignments. No matter who does the alignments, the assistant is responsible for making sure they are correct and complete. Most engineers won't even check the alignments, taking the trusted assistant's word that they are correct. Frankly, a few engineers will come in, crouch down in front of the machine and examine every meter, fanatically making sure each track is aligned exactly.

PLAYBACK ALIGNMENT

Loading the Machine

Begin the alignment by loading the tone reel on the machine. Commercially available tone reel tapes contain various alignment tones recorded at a specific operating level. Whether the tone reel is ¼", ½", 1", or 2", the tones are recorded across the width of the tape, making it essentially a one-track tape. For example, a 2" tone reel can be used to align 2" 16-track or 24-track heads.

There are different playback equalization standards in different parts of the world. European (IEC), and North American (NAB) standards differ. There are many fine books available that explain all about the differences in equalization standards. This ain't one of 'em. To begin the alignment:

1) Remove the reel of tape from the box, place it on the take-up spindle of the multitrack machine, and tighten the locks. The right side, the take-up side, takes up the tape during playback. The left side, the supply side, supplies the tape during playback.

2) If a collar is holding the end of the tape in place, remove it and place it nearby. If a piece of adhesive tape is holding the end of the tape to the reel, stick it on the corner of the multitrack machine so you can use it again when you're finished with the reel.

3) Before threading the tape, place a matching sized empty take-up reel on the supply side. Different sized reels can create a torquing imbalance that is hard on the motors, and may cause speed fluctuations and tape spillage.

4) Guide the tail end of the tape through the tape path, across the heads, and through the capstan rollers to the empty supply side.

5) If the very end bit of tape is wrinkled or torn at all, splice it off. The empty reel will grasp the end section of tape much better if the tape is clean and wrinkle free.

6) After threading, replace the head protector to avoid hum.

7) Retrace the tape path, checking that it is correct before engaging the transport of the machine. If the tape is re-wound while threaded incorrectly, you may easily do damage to: 1) the machine, 2) the tape, 3) your credibility.

8) If the empty reel is slightly bent, the tape may rub against the inside. When this happens, remove the reel, and turn it over. If the rub remains, replace the empty reel with another one.

9) Rewind the alignment tape to the section containing 1khz. and park it there. The machine is now ready for the playback alignment.

Playback Levels

The heads on most professional multitrack analog machines have three alignable sections. The *repro* section, sometimes called playback, the *sync* section, sometimes called sel-sync and the *record* section. The *azimuth* (the perpendicular angle of the head) should also be checked, but this is usually done by the technical staff. Start with the repro section, then do the sync section, and finally the record section.

Before starting the alignment, make sure you understand exactly what you are doing. When the machine is incorrectly aligned, problems may not be immediately noticed. Level differences will definitely be noticed when the machine is correctly aligned for your next session.

As you begin the alignment, make sure VSO and noise reduction are off, and all connections to and from the machine are correct. Some newer machines aren't aligned using a screwdriver, but are electronically aligned using push-buttons. If your studio doesn't have these machines, find the correct alignment tool and begin. The alignment pots in the machines can sometimes get dust in them, and need to be cleaned. Do this by inserting the alignment tool and carefully working the alignment pots back and forth. Remember, occasionally clean the pots in the sync!

2db or not 2db

Recent advancements in tape technology now allow increased headroom, so elevated recording levels are achievable. This means that today's tapes can withstand hotter signal before saturation, which causes distortion. Studios have begun increasing the level to tape by aligning machines to at least +3db over the 250nwb/m standard, and sometimes even higher.

Not to get too technical, but a 3db change is a change of half power. Because the decibel is simply a ratio of one number to another, if you had 250 of one item, say apples, and you added 3db (half of 250) of apples, you would have about 375 apples. If you added 6db of apples to the 250, you would have about 500 apples. (The term decibel refers to sound levels, not pieces of fruit.)

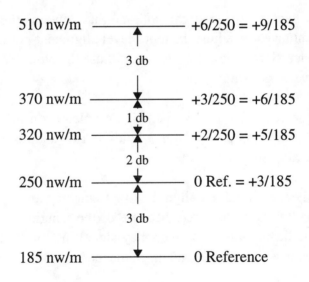

Figure 4.1. NanoWebers/Meter to Decibels

With this in mind while doing the alignment, if the engineer wants the alignment levels elevated to 370nwb/m, rather than the standard 250nwb/m, the levels on the meters are brought up by 3db. Do this by aligning the levels to -3 VU on the meters, not 0 VU. This then requires an additional 3db of level to bring signal up to 0 VU. Use the enclosed graph to see where 370nwb/m is compared to the level of the alignment reel. Figure 4.1. Notice that the elevated standards levels on the graph are an industry standard and not *exactly* half. To align the machine:

1) Put the machine in *repro* and turn the main monitor down. Tones don't need to be loud to be heard.

2) Turn off all master sends. Tones will be sent to the inputs of any outboard equipment normalled from any sends that happen to be turned up. As well, the sends to headphones must be off, or else the tones may blast out the elements. Either turn them down, or deadpatch the cue sends at the patchbay. (See Chapter Six for more on deadpatching.)

3) Find the section of the alignment tape that contains the 1khz. tone. Play the alignment tape and adjust the repro level alignment pot for track 1 to 0 VU on each meter. Some recording studios still use the old reference of 700hz. for the repro level alignment.

4) When the repro level alignment is completed on all tracks, transport the alignment tape to the section that holds 10khz. and do the same alignment on the high-frequency repro pots.

5) Note that you should not align the low frequency level (50hz. or 100hz.) with the full track alignment reel because of the fringing effect. Fringing occurs when the heads draw low frequency signal in from outside the normal tape path, giving an inaccurate reading on the meters.

6) After aligning the repro high frequency alignment, transport the tape back to the 1khz. section of the alignment tape.

7) Change the operating status of the multitrack machine to *sync* and re-do the same level and high frequency alignment procedure, adjusting the sync pots.

8) When repro and sync are aligned, transport the alignment tape off, and replace the collar on the tone reel. When no collar is available, use the small strip of adhesive tape mentioned earlier.

9) Remove the tone reel from the machine and put it away. Because you will usually make a new tone reel for large project, the commercial tone reel will not be used for the rest of the project.

Removing a Reel/Packing

When you rewind or fast-forward a tape on a reel, the high speeds can cause it to pack unevenly, leaving the outside edges exposed, perhaps losing the integrity of the edge tracks. When tapes are played off, or slow wound to the end of the reel, they pack smoothly and evenly. Digital tapes aren't as susceptible to this uneven packing, and can usually be rewound without worry of exposed edges.

Some multitrack machines have a slow wind feature, allowing the tape to pack evenly as it winds off. Some machines also have an auto torquing feature that slows the transport down when nearing the end of the reel.

When you are quickly changing reels during a busy session, there may be little time to slow wind the reel off. Fast-forward the reel off. Later, when you have enough time, re-load the tape, rewind it to the beginning of last song worked on, and slow wind it off, making sure the packing is smooth and uniform. Perhaps use a second multitrack machine during the session, if one is available.

All tapes destined for long-term storage must be slow wound and packed smoothly. Whether rewinding or fast forwarding, avoid letting any reel go so fast that it whips off the end of the reel loudly flapping until it finally stops. No one wants to see their tapes mishandled.

RECORD ALIGNMENT

Loading and Exercising

Remove a virgin analog reel from the box, take it out of the plastic bag, and set the tape on the take-up side spindle. This reel will be dedicated as the tone reel and used for the record alignment. This is usually reel 1 of a project, and will hold the tones, the record pad, and sometimes the tuning tones. This reel should be the same brand, model number and batch as the rest of the reels used for the project. Remove the sticker with the batch number from the end of the reel, and stick it inside the tape box. This sticker must be kept for reference, in case any problems arise with the tape.

Some engineers want virgin tape exercised before first use. This doesn't mean taking the tape out for a stroll around the lake, it means to align the packing, or tension of a virgin tape with the torque of the machine. Sort of letting the virgin tape and the machine go around for a while before starting basics. To exercise the tape:

1) Put the virgin reel upside down on the take-up side of the multitrack machine, and an empty reel on the supply side.

2) Thread the tape, re-zero the tape counter, and completely rewind the reel.

3) Re-thread the tape and wind it to the beginning. Some engineers feel that the beginning of the tape may retain some residual magnetism left by the large blade used at the tape factory. Splice off the first few feet of tape at the beginning and splice in a foot or two of leader. Check before inserting leaders, as some engineers want no leaders. (A leader is a strip of paper or plastic inserted between separate sections of tape to keep track of all recordings.) You should now be at the top of the reel and ready to do the record alignment.

If a client arrives with a single virgin reel to be recorded on, load the reel upside down on the take-up side of the machine, thread it, and rewind it all the way off to another reel. Turn the now empty original reel over, and re-thread the tape. When the session ends, the client's tape will be tails out, packed evenly, and on his original reel.

Oscillator

Most desks have a built-in oscillator (a pure sine wave generator with a full range of frequencies and gain control) accessible in the patchbay. The oscillator is used to align the tape machines, test signal flow, set unity gain, and trace down problems.

Biasing

Begin the record alignment with the biasing. Bias, a very high-frequency tone somewhere close to 150khz. is recorded with the audio signal to help it bond to tape.

Remember when you were a kid at the circus, and you would buy a little tin heart with a little tin chain for that special someone. The fat guy with no neck behind the booth would use an electric pencil to engrave "To Mila, From Tim" on it. The pencil's tip would vibrate so fast that it would dig right into the tin. Without that high frequency vibration, the tip of the engraving pen would only scratch the surface of the tin. This concept is the general principle behind tape biasing. The high-frequency tone recorded with the audio signal vastly increases the tape retention.

1) To set bias, turn the desk oscillator on. Most studios use 10khz., however some use 15khz. or 1khz. Whatever is standard where you work is the right way. This tone is the carrier frequency used to set bias.

2) Put all tracks in *record-ready*. Some multitrack machines have an *auto-input* mode which, when pressed, automatically switches all tracks in record-ready to input mode. For this application, switch the machine to repro mode. The machine should now be in repro, with all tracks in record-ready.

3) Record the tone on all tracks.

4) Some machines have a bias pot for each track, and some machines have a single bias pot for the entire machine. As you record, turn the bias pot all the way down (counter-clockwise) then slowly bring it up, watching the meters. The needle will rise past zero and into the red, reach its highest point, then descend again.

5) Continue turning clockwise, allowing the needle to descend from 1 to 4db from the highest point on the VU meter, depending on the tape used and the studio overbias standard. This overbiasing has proven to increase sound quality.

6) Now begin the record alignment.

Record Alignment

To begin the record alignment, rewind to where the alignment tones will be recorded: after the first leader on the tone reel.

1) Set the oscillator at 1khz. and leave all tracks on the multitrack machine in record-ready. Switch the multitrack machine to *auto-input*. This should put all tracks on the multitrack machine in *input* mode. Keep the machine in input to check input levels.

2) Adjust the output level of the oscillator to 0 VU on the meters of the machine.

3) With the machine in repro mode, press record, and adjust the record level to 0 VU on all tracks. As you adjust this pot, monitor the repro level, which is aligned correctly because you just did it. When the record level reaches 0 VU, the record input level matches the repro output level.

4) When the record level is aligned on all tracks, change frequencies on the oscillator to 10khz.

5) Adjust the record high frequency pots to 0 VU.

6) Change the oscillator to low frequency (50hz. or 100hz.) and continue recording while adjusting the repro level of those low frequencies. As there are, say, 24 individual tracks of low frequency instead of one full track, there is now no signal on the tape between the individual tracks, defeating the fringing effect.

7) After completing the alignment, mark a corner of the machine with the alignment level, tape speed, the brand and model number of tape the machine was biased for, the project, the date, and your name. This information is included in case someone wants to question or comment about the alignment.

DIGITAL MULTITRACK ALIGNMENT

If recording with digital machines, set the correct machine settings according to the session. As digital machines do not have a repro and a sync, simply record a set of tones as described in Chapter Eleven.

CREATING A TONE REEL

After completing the record alignment, go to the beginning of the tone reel. Record at least 60 seconds each of 1khz., 10khz., 15khz., 100hz., and 50hz. After these tones, install at least a two-minute section of record pad. (The record pad is a section of tape used for doing a daily record alignment.) These tones and pad are then leadered, clearly labeled, and used for all future alignments on this project.

Of course, as the tones may take up to five or six minutes worth of tape, the rest of the reel can still be used for recording. Some projects leave the tones, record pad, and tuning tones on a separate reel, with nothing else on the reel.

When the tones reside on a reel that also contains program (anything recorded on tape) put the tones at the end of the reel, with the record pad last on the reel. As the reels are stored tails out, finding the tones is faster if they are at the end of the reel, not at the beginning.

If the tones are at the head of the reel, the record pad falls right before the first song on the reel. As the record pad is used daily for the alignment, all it takes is one momentary lapse of concentration to let the tape roll past the leader and record over the intro of the first song on the reel. If this ever occurs, I'm sure the gas station will give you your old job back.

AFTER THE ALIGNMENT

After the alignment is complete, load the first reel to be recorded, and transport it to the correct spot where the recording will begin. If the reel is virgin, go to the beginning of the exersized reel. If the reel is not virgin, go to the end of the last song on tape. Make sure there is enough tape for a complete pass. If there is only a few minutes left on the reel, ask the engineer if he wants you to load a virgin reel instead.

Once the correct reel is loaded, put all tracks in *record-ready*. The machine is now ready for recording.

Checking Each Reel

Often, as record levels to tape may vary slightly from reel to reel, even within a batch, some engineers want each virgin analog reel tested before use. Sessions can go through many reels, so checking the record alignment for each reel must be fast. To check the alignment for each reel:

1) After loading and exercising the virgin reel, quickly record a small amount of 1khz., 10khz., and 100hz. at the head. If the sync and repro levels coming back aren't consistent with the alignment, bring it to the engineer's attention.

2) If you come across a bad reel, tell the engineer. He will want to use a different reel, or maybe even a different batch.

3) As tones tend not to erase totally when recorded over, cut off the section of tape used for these tones.

4) Turn on the oscillator when the musicians have either removed their headphones or, more advisable, when the signal has been cut off from the cue sends.

Don't let anyone in the session hear alignment tones, or tone from the oscillator. If you are alone in the control room, use the speakers to hear tones. However if a client is there, use headphones. If you must use speakers, keep the gain low, because anyone in this industry knows that a good loud blast of 10,000hz. hurts.

TAPES FROM OTHER STUDIOS

Tapes previously recorded at other studios may arrive with no tones, and no mention of levels. Contact the studio where the tapes originated, and get the proper information from the assistant who worked on the project. The assistant's name should be on a tracksheet or tape label. If you cannot trace the information, load the tape and try to figure out the level. Watch how the meters are reacting. If the signal appears very low, the overall level needs to be brought up. If the signal appears very high and all meters are in the red, then realign using a lower level.

When the client brings the tapes to the session, of course you can't check the alignment until he arrives. This often leaves little time for a complete alignment. If you're in a hurry, there may be no time to align all tracks.

When you're doing an overdub session, tracks containing bass and drums will probably not be recorded on, so these tracks may not need a record alignment. However, a complete alignment is always recommended over a partial one.

. . . .

Summary

Chapter Four explained how to handle tapes and machines for a session:

- Placement of the machines for optimum use.

- Bringing all the tapes into the studio.

- Cleaning, demagnetizing and aligning of the tape machines.

- Creating a tone reel for alignments on your project.

CHAPTER FIVE

. . . .

Outboard And Speakers

OUTBOARD EQUIPMENT

In the recording studio, the outboard equipment includes all external processing devices not housed within the desk. This equipment, such as equalizers, limiters, delays, samplers, echo plates and reverbs is used when additional signal processing is needed, either for recording, mixing or monitoring.

You are expected know what outboard equipment the studio has, how to access all settings, store custom programs and, most importantly, explain it all to the engineer. If necessary, keep a section in your daily log with a few reminders or tips on operating unfamiliar equipment. (See Chapter Seven for more on daily log.)

Whenever new equipment arrives, the manuals that come with them are extremely helpful. They keep the engineer busy while you get in there and learn how the new equipment works. When clients are paying massive amounts of money to rent a studio and hire a big gun engineer, they don't want to be waiting around because no one knows how to use the new piece of outboard.

STANDARD OUTBOARD RACKS

Most studios have stationary racks that contain the standard outboard equipment. These racks always stay in the control room and are located where the engineer can easily reach the controls. The equipment is usually hard wired to the patchbay, and is included in the base rate of the studio.

Engineers expect the studio to supply a reasonable amount of outboard equipment. Often a piece of outboard equipment gets removed from the control room because it's being held for another session, or it's malfunctioning. If any standard outboard has been pulled, find out why before your session. The studio will usually replace unavailable equipment with something comparable.

Additional Outboard

When the engineer needs additional outboard equipment for the session, it usually may be rented from the studio or from a local equipment rental company, often at additional cost to the client. Keep a current list of the studio's rental equipment, sometimes called floaters, and equipment available from local rental companies.

Outboard equipment not permanently mounted in stationary racks are usually housed in standard 19-inch-wide road cases for protection while in transit, and for ease of stacking. Figure 5.1. These cases usually leave an inch or two at top and bottom of the case, and sometimes have a small fan to keep the equipment cool. The equipment stays in the case, and the front and back panels are removed to access the controls and connections. The proper cables and power cords are usually included.

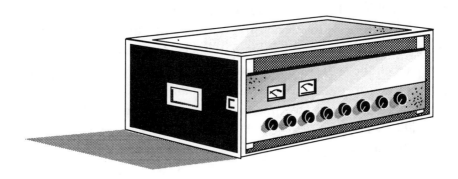

Figure 5.1. Standard Outboard Rack

Sometimes the engineer may bring his own rack(s) of outboard, all programmed with his favorite settings. This is not only convenient for the engineer, but usually cheaper for the client than renting additional outboard for the duration of a project. Some of these racks are set up with power strips and mini patchbays, making setup even easier.

Renting Equipment

For many sessions, additional outboard equipment, microphones, cables, stands, modules, etc., must be rented. Audio rental companies have almost all equipment available today and, in major cities, many deliver 24 hours a day. Keep lists with audio equipment rental companies and telephone numbers to neighboring studios nearby, in case anything needs to be rented or borrowed.

Before ordering items from the rental companies, verify the rental costs with the producer to avoid unforeseen problems. When the equipment arrives, you or someone will sign for it. Verify that the serial numbers on the invoice correspond to equipment received, and that all manuals and cables are included. Make a note of any scratches or dents.

PLACEMENT AND CONNECTION

Whether the additional equipment being used is the engineer's own equipment, a floater, or a rental, it needs to be correctly placed in the control room. Before bringing the equipment into the control room, make a space where the engineer can comfortably reach the settings. Most studios have space for outboard cases to be placed next to the desk, or behind the engineer. If an equalizer is half way across the control room, and off to one side, the engineer must move out of the main sound field area, and may not be able to hear the slight changes being made. To set up this additional outboard equipment:

• Bring the cases containing the outboard equipment into the control room, and remove the front and back panels before stacking them. You don't want to stack them up, only to find the bottom one is upside down.

As you remove the panels, label them with the name of the unit from which they were removed, and whether they are front or back panels. Then put them away.

• When the rental is for an extended project, the engineer may want the units placed within the stationary rack. If the equipment is only rented for a few days, the front and back panels may be put in studio storage, rather than left in the control room.

• If many cases are brought in, don't stack them too high on top of each other. This may create a sound block and change the acoustics of one side of the audio spectrum. Also, it is very easy to bump into an unstable stack of these expensive and delicate items, creating a veritable "Fourth of July" when they come crashing down with sparks flying and black smoke everywhere. It's even more enjoyable when someone else does it.

Power Up or Down

Many pieces of equipment may be plugged in at one small area where all the outlets are, so use care when plugging or unplugging power. Accidentally unplugging the power cord of an active piece of outboard equipment might not be an issue at the beginning of a session, but may cause problems toward the end of a session, especially a mixdown session. As most digital equipment doesn't retain specific settings during power down, any settings being used will be lost unless they were stored internally. If the unit is active in the monitors when powering up or down, mute the returns on the desk to avoid a great pop. This pop usually blows speakers, fuses, and minds.

Most pieces of equipment have a removable power cable. Before connecting the power cable to the equipment, label it at the plug end with the name of the equipment it connects to. This ensures its proper return. You will be glad you did when you are crawling around trying to find an open outlet, or tracing a power cable to find where it originates. If you get in the habit of keeping the proper cord with the proper unit, you will never lose the cord — unless, of course, you lose the entire unit.

Back Panel

Sometimes outboard equipment not connected to the bay has to be accessed at the back of the piece of equipment itself. This means crawling behind the outboard rack, cables in hand, whenever the engineer decides he wants a change. Depending on his needs, you may have to connect the equipment to the patchbay, or to other outboard.

Connecting different pieces of outboard equipment can be challenging, since different equipment manufacturers sometimes use different input and output formats, with assorted wiring combinations. Most professional outboard equipment has either XLR or ¼" connections, and both may have different pin wiring configurations. The technical staff might need to create special cables with various connectors at both ends to accommodate all connections. If you can, use the balanced XLR connections.

Most outboard equipment has one or two inputs, and two or four outputs. Some have more, and all will be labeled with their proper function.

Before connecting the unit, ask the engineer which inputs and outputs he prefers. Tell him if there is any additional level or equalization controls on the back panel that he might not know about. If he is not there to ask, connect the unit as you see fit, and check with him when he arrives.

Connections

Outboard equipment that always stays in the control room can usually be accessed at the patchbay. Some studios label the patchbay, showing where all the outboard appears. Other studios label the individual pieces of outboard equipment with the corresponding patch point numbers at the bay. Others keep a list next to the desk showing each piece of outboard equipment, and its corresponding patch point numbers. When the engineer needs a certain piece of equipment, you can look at the numbers on the list, find the corresponding patch points in the patchbay, and make the patch. (See Chapter Six for more on patching.)

Many studios have input panels in the control room that are wired directly to the patchbay. When additional outboard equipment is brought in, connect it to the patchbay through these input panels via short XLR cables. Either label the new piece of outboard equipment with its patch point numbers, or add the numbers to the current outboard list.

TESTING SIGNAL FLOW

Once a piece of additional outboard is placed, connected and turned on, double check the inputs and outputs, the sends and returns from the desk, and the left/right integrity. The left cable must be on the left side, and the right cable must be on the right side. Connect the outboard equipment properly before the engineer tries to use it and finds out it isn't working. Listen to the returns to see if the unit is correctly grounded. Occasionally, if a unit has a buzz or hum, it needs to be grounded. (See Chapter Three for more on grounding.) The old line in the studio is that the reason the unit is humming is because it doesn't know the words. This usually has the client reeling with laughter.

Use the oscillator to trace the signal path to make sure everything is properly connected. We will delve deeper into the patchbay later, but for now, do these few simple patches. Some engineers want you to set the input and output levels at unity gain using the oscillator.

Unity Gain

Unity gain is simply equipment's input level matching its output level. To set unity gain, patch out of the oscillator, and into a nearby input meter. The meters on the multitrack machine should be close and convenient. Set the oscillator output level at 0 VU according to the meter on the machine. Patch out of the oscillator and into the piece of outboard then back into the input meter on the machine. Set the input and output levels of the outboard to read 0 VU.

You may also want to check each channel on the desk to make sure that 0 VU on the channel fader actually is 0 VU on the channel meter. This works for limiters, equalizers and delays, but for echo plates or reverbs a pure tone may not give an accurate reading, so if possible, use white noise to set the levels. (See later in this chapter for more on white noise.) Once the outboard is set up and checked for proper connection, zero all outboard equipment that might be used during the session (return all switches and knobs to their standard off position.)

Reset

Most units have a reset button to be used when the unit freezes. This button, surprisingly enough, resets the unit to its original factory specifications, losing all the stored programs that you and everyone else have so painstakingly created. If the unit needs resetting, first try turning it off and then on. As a last resort, press the reset button. Of course, mute the returns before doing this.

STUDIO TIE LINES

Many recording studios have more than one control room, and each control room must keep adequate outboard equipment for sessions to proceed. Invariably, when working in one control room, the engineer also wants to use equipment from the other control room. One option is to remove the outboard from the other studio, bring it in, and set it up for your session. Check with the studio manager before removing any equipment from another control room. Even if the other room is not in use, another session may be scheduled to start before your session ends.

Another option is to connect equipment in another control room through tie lines. Tie lines connect all the patchbays within a premises, so that equipment in one control room can be accessed from another. All equipment can theoretically stay where it is, and be used for any session in any control room. Of course, someone has to go to the other control room to make the patches and set the levels — usually you. Larger equipment, such as an echo plate, is usually kept in a distant closet and connected through tie lines.

CLICK GENERATORS

A click is often sent through the headphones to help the musicians keep the timing of each song consistent through all takes. Without it, slight tempo changes may occur from the first take to the last. However, some musicians are opposed to playing along with such a rigid time structure, and prefer to let the natural flow of the music guide the tempo.

A click can be generated by anything from a microphone on a metronome to a complete set of electronic drums. Unlike most outboard equipment, click generators don't have an audio input. They can be driven by other codes, but it isn't a send and return situation. A click generator is also used to help the engineer edit the multitrack tape from one take to another, and for very basic synchronization.

Operation and setup of click can get complicated, as there may be timecode that goes with the click to drive a sequencer. Click and timecode are recorded on separate tracks. (See Chapter Nine for more on timecodes.)

To set up a click, either patch directly out of the click generator into the multitrack machine or bring it up in a channel on the desk, and assign it to the multitrack. The click track is sent to the musicians through the cue sends, the same as any other track.

The drummer may have the click generator with him in the studio, or it may be in the control room. However it is set up, the engineer must set the level to head-phones and to tape. If the click generator is in the control room, you may have to start and stop the click generators, as the engineer has more important things to do. Label the track sheet with the correct BPM (beats per minute.)

Whenever printing a click to tape, keep the level low, around -10db, as the high transients tend to leak into neighboring tracks, wreaking havoc on adjacent timecode tracks. If you find high transients leaking in your studio, talk to the manager about beefing up security.

VIDEO

Some studios are laid out in such a way that the control room can't be seen from the studio, so video cameras sometimes link the control room and the studio. Place the camera(s) where the control room can monitor the widest area of the studio. Place the video monitor at an appropriate spot in the control room, often between the speakers, in front of the desk. You must understand how these are connected, so you can do the setup whenever necessary.

Video is not always used simply to monitor the studio activities. For movie and television soundtracks and jingle sessions, the audio being recorded is synchronized to a prerecorded video. As the musicians watch the video monitor, they play along with it. The music is then synchronized with the video. This lets the producer see and hear how the audio and video work together. Music video makers tend to do the opposite, making the video after the audio is recorded.

SPEAKERS

Most control rooms have a pair of large permanently mounted studio monitors aimed at the center of the desk where the engineer sits. All control rooms have at least one set of studio near field monitors sitting on the desk at ear level. (Technically, the term "monitor" normally refers to the complete unit, and the term "speaker" refers to the cone, but commonly, the whole unit is called the speaker.) These are often referred to as the main speakers and the mini speakers, or simply upstairs and downstairs. Many engineers get used to a certain make and model of mini speaker, and always use that particular one in the studio. They either bring their own, or specify to the studio which ones to have available for the session.

REMOVAL AND REPLACEMENT

Sometimes, speakers in the control room need to be replaced. If the studio owns the mini speakers, matching replacement speakers should be somewhere on the premises. Don't remove a speaker from another control room without authorization. To replace or add speakers for the session:

1) Remove all tapes from the vicinity before bringing any speakers into the control room. Speakers have magnets and magnets erase tapes.

2) Mute the gain on the desk. Some studios even have you turn the amplifiers off before disconnecting speakers.

3) If replacing the present speakers, unhook the wires, remembering, or even writing down, which wires were on which terminal.

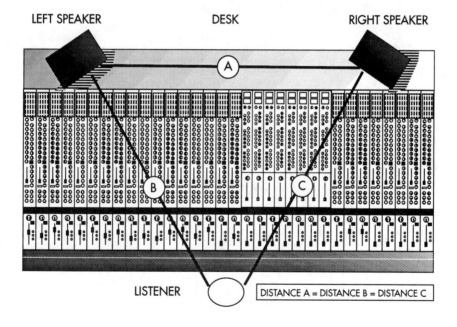

Figure 5.2. Equilateral Triangle

4) If the grilles (the protective covers on the front of the speakers, often cloth) have been removed, find them and fasten them to the front of the speaker casing. Remove the speakers and place them on the floor next to the desk. Face them inward, toward each other, so the cones won't accidentally get kicked in.

5) Bring in the replacement speakers. Remove them from their cases if necessary, and set them where the old ones were. If you are not replacing the speakers, but simply adding additional speakers, set them on matching stands close to the existing ones. There should be additional cables from the amplifier to connect to these speakers.

6) Place the speakers so the tweeters face out or up. Some engineers will want the grilles removed.

7) Connect the cables to the back of the speakers, making sure the phase is correct, and the left cable is on the left speaker, and the right cable is on the right speaker. Correct phase occurs when the grounding wire within each cable is connected to the same post on both speakers.

8) Place the speakers creating an equilateral triangle between them and the listener. Figure 5.2. Sit in the engineer's chair to check for exact placement.

9) All speakers should have fuses installed so that a power surge will blow the fuse before the speaker. If the speaker is fatigued, the fuse may not protect it from blowing. At times, the engineer will monitor loud enough to blow a speaker, or a power surge on the line will move so fast that both the fuse and the speaker will blow simultaneously.

   However, some engineers feel that fuses change the sound of the speaker, and do not use them. They monitor at their own risk. If the engineer blows an expensive speaker, *he* may have a power surge.

10) Turn the amplifiers on and listen to a familiar song to check that the speakers are working and properly connected. Listen to the high, mid, and low frequencies to make sure the speakers are working correctly on both sides.

11) If no signal at all is coming out of a speaker, check the fuse. If it is blown, lower the gain and replace it with a matching fuse.

While replacing mini speakers is routine in the studio, changing main studio speakers is not. This is a job usually handled by the technical staff. When the main speakers do need to be changed, help the technical staff with the change just for the experience.

Additional Speakers

Some sessions require a single speaker between the main stereo pair to monitor in mono. Other sessions, such as movie soundtracks, use five or more speakers. No matter what unusual speaker configuration is used, you should know why and how it's hooked up that way.

Some mix machines have a tiny speaker in the meter bridge, which is used to monitor signal on tape or input to the machine. Some engineers check the sound of their mixes through these tiny mono speakers. This gives an indication of how the mix will come across on a tiny radio or television speaker. If it comes across well on the radio, it's a hit. To heck with melody, musicianship and talent, it's gotta *sound good.*

Speakers for Cue

In the studio, some singers prefer to use speakers instead of headphones for their cue mix. This is usually so the singer can hear himself without the bulk of headphones. Set up correctly, very little leakage from the speakers will be recorded to tape. Figure 5.3.

To set this up, place two small matching speakers at ear level in front of the singer, forming an equilateral triangle between the speakers and the microphone. With one speaker out-of-phase with the other, send a mono cue send. These signals cancel each other when they reach the microphone. If the singer is standing in the proper spot in the studio the song being played is heard, but not recorded. The sound for the singer is a bit odd, as everything is out of phase.

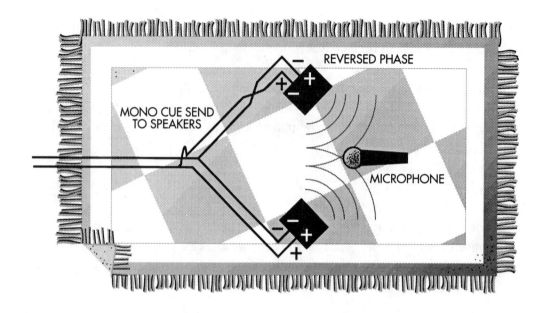

Figure 5.3. Studio Speaker Cue setup

In the control room, some musicians like a pair of speakers directly in front of them as they record. This may give the added impact needed to get the creative juices flowing. The musician may be off axis to the main monitors, but having speakers directly in front of him lets him hear everything clear and up front. In this situation there is no microphone in use, so signal leakage to tape is not a concern.

ANALYZATION AND EQUALIZATION

Control rooms are occasionally analyzed with a spectrum analyzer to check the frequency response. White noise (a wide band noise with equal energy per octave) is sent through the large studio monitors, and the analyzer displays the control room's frequency highs and lows. Any errant frequencies are then added or removed with external equalization to get the flattest frequency response. The equalizer used is usually housed near the main amplifiers, and is set by either the chief engineer, or head of technical. While a spectrum analyzer gives a general view of how the control room sounds, most engineers will set the monitor equalization with their ears, using the analyzer only as a reference.

Many small speakers have an equalizer control in or on them. Don't change these settings unless the engineer tells you to. When the settings must be changed, write the setting down on a piece of paper. Again, don't make a pencil mark on someone's equipment or instrument.

. . . .

Summary

Chapter Five explained how to handle outboard equipment and speakers for a session:

- Placement and connection of standard outboard equipment racks.

- Setup and use of click generators.

- Placement and connection of speakers in the control room and studio.

- Control room analyzation and equalization.

CHAPTER SIX

. . . .

Desk And Patchbay

As you may have realized, this book is not an equipment manual, so full details of equipment operations and audio terms are not included. You will find no explanation of intermodulation distortion in this book. While it does not explain how everything works, it does try to emphasize the importance of understanding all the equipment in the studio, especially the desk.

The desk, also called the console, or board, is the heart of the studio. It combines all input signals, processes them, and sends these combined signals to a recording machine and/or monitor system. There are many different makes and models of boards, from very large and complex to quite simple.

Most desks are broken down into three sections: The *input* section is where the signal reaches the desk and is processed. The *monitor* section is either the live inputs from the studio, or the returns from the multitrack machine. The *center* section houses the master sends and returns, the main studio gain, the talkback section, the oscillator, and access to monitoring other external sources in the control room, such as cassette machines. Desks within a make and model operate the same way in any studio. Although the desks may be the same, the rest of the studio is probably not.

NORMALS

While many signal connections need to be routed at the patchbay, some signal flow is normalled. A normal in the studio is a signal's standard hard wired route. Common normals in a studio are sends and returns. For example, send 1 may be normalled to echo plate 1, then returning to stereo return 1. If you turn up send 1 on any channel, and that signal will go to the echo plate, and back to the normalled return without being patched. Figure 6.1. shows the flow of a signal's standard hard wired route, and full and half patch points. Notice the input and output of the send, and the input and output of the return can be accessed at the patchbay.

Also normalled are the inputs and outputs of the desk. Depending on the mode of the desk, the channel inputs might be normalled from the microphones or from the returns of the multitrack machine. (See later in this chapter for the desk's different modes.) These normals are just examples: your studio might be set up differently.

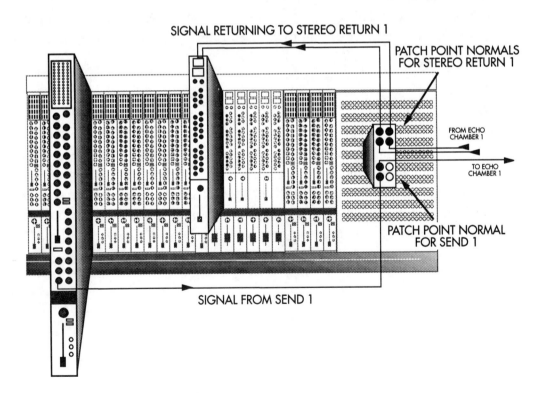

Figure 6.1. Normals in the Patchbay

BREAKING THE NORMALS

All normals have access points at the patchbay, and can be re-routed. Still, just because a normal signal is re-routed does not necessarily mean it stops going to its original destination.

Full normal patch points totally interrupt the signal flow at both the output and input patch points. In most patchbays, only the microphone inputs and outputs are full normal. If you insert a patchcord into the output of, for instance, microphone patch point 1, the signal flow is interrupted. The microphone signal does *not* proceed on its standard path on to channel 1.

Half normal patch points allow re-routing of the signal without interrupting the existing signal flow. For example, if you patch from the outputs of echo chamber 3 into channel line inputs 27 and 28 on the desk, because the outputs of the stereo return are half normalled, the signal continues to return to stereo return 3, as well as to line inputs 27 and 28. If you don't want the signal to return to stereo return 3, you must deadpatch the inputs of stereo return 3. (A deadpatch is a patchcord connected to the input of a normal, used to interrupt the standard normal signal path.)

THE DESK

While many engineers want to set the equalization and outboard settings them-selves, most expect the assistant engineer to complete the bussing and patching before they arrive for the session. The engineer should be able to come in, sit at the desk and be assured that everything is complete and correct according to his specifications on the input/setup sheet.

ZEROING THE DESK

Before starting a session, the desk needs to be zeroed and cleaned. Zeroing the desk means returning all the knobs, faders, and subgroups to their standard off position. This should have been done by the assistant from the previous session, as you will do at the end of your session. Dust off the surface of the desk, and erase any pencil marks or grease marks.

LABELING THE STRIP

After zeroing the desk, label the scribble strip, commonly known as simply the strip. The strip is the area of the desk above the faders, used to write the individual channel information. Run either a length of one-inch paper leader or, more popular, a length of white adhesive tape across the desk strip. Both can be removed and kept for future sessions within a project. It is inconvenient to totally re-write the strip every time the song is changed.

As each song has its own strip, when the song is changed the strip is also changed, then updated as more instruments are recorded. This strip is used until the song is mixed, when another strip is made to suit the engineer's choice of track layouts. (See Chapter Eleven for more on mixing.)

To retain the stickiness of the adhesive tape, store the strips on the glass partitions between the studio and control room — of course without blocking out the engineer's view of the studio. When the project is over, roll up the strips of tape and keep them with the rest of the paperwork.

When leader or adhesive tape is not used for the strip, china markers, or erasable felt pens are used to write directly on the desk strip. However you label the desk, here are a few guidelines:

- Write on the strip the way the engineer does. He may prefer different instruments or functions written in different colors, or double-thick strips of tape, or perhaps a line drawn between each input. Figure 6.2.

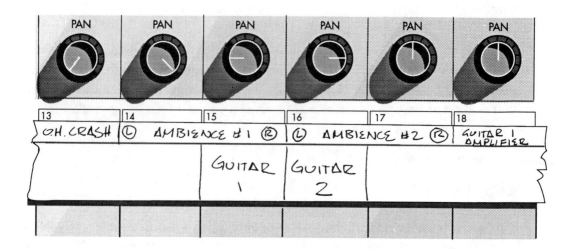

Figure 6.2. The Strip Label

- Sometimes running adhesive tape across the strip hides the channel numbers on the desk. Write the channel number on the corner of each input, or place the tape low enough on the strip so as not to cover the numbers.

- Sometimes the strip must contain both the inputs to, and the returns from, the multitrack machine, so you may need to write a lot of information on the small space allotted. When the channel is being used as a microphone input, mark down the instrument, the microphone and, if used, the microphone pad.

- Write the part, for example "chorus guitar," and sometimes the musician. Four channels of accordion might need the name of each musician on the strip. One drummer wouldn't.

- For an effects return, label the send, the effect, and perhaps the length or depth of the unit. For example "Send 1—Echo Plate 1—2.5 seconds."

19	20	21	22	23	24
GUITAR 1 DIRECT	GUITAR 2	(L) KEYBOARD #1 (R)		(L) KEYBOARD #2 (R)	
KEYBOARDS				CLICK	

DESK MODE

Before you continue with the setup of the desk, switch it to the correct operating mode. Most desks operate in two main mode's: *microphone* (also called *record* mode) and *line* (also called *mix* mode.) In microphone mode, the input panel inputs are normalled to each channel on the desk. For example, a microphone plugged into input 12 in the studio is normalled to the main fader on channel 12 on the desk. Basics are often recorded in this mode.

In line mode, the main faders are not microphone inputs, but line inputs, such as returns from the multitrack machine, or returns from outboard equipment. For example, track 12 on the multitrack machine is normalled to track 12 on the desk. Sometimes these returns are not normalled to the desk, and need to be patched. Overdubs and mixing are often done in this mode.

As the status of the whole desk can be changed from one mode to the other, so can the individual channels. For example, with the desk in microphone mode, the click generator might be introduced into the channel at line level. This channel is changed from microphone to line mode using a *flip* button.

Some desks operate in tandem with the multitrack machines. The multitrack machine's sync and repro modes, as well as the individual tracks, are accessed from within the desk. For example, if track 18 is to be recorded, a button on channel 18 on the desk is pressed to activate *record-ready* on the multitrack machine. With the desk in the correct mode, begin the bussing using the input/setup sheet (fig. 2.1.).

BUSSING

The busses, sometimes called group outputs, are the numbered buttons on each channel of the desk. Busses are sends that normally route signal from the individual channels on the desk to the tracks on the multitrack machine. For example, if buss 3 on channel 14 is pressed, signal from channel 14 is sent to, and recorded on track 3, unless the signal path is broken at the patchbay. Some smaller 8-buss consoles use cross-normalling, which routes signal from buss 1 to tracks 1, 9, and 17 without using patchcords. The buss outputs are accessed at the patchbay, so they can also be used to send signal to outboard effects.

According to the input/setup sheet (fig. 2.1.), most of the instruments are bussed to single tracks. However, notice that the overhead microphones in inputs 11, 12 and 13 are bussed to tracks 9 and 10. The engineer wants a stereo spread of the crash cymbal overhead microphones (inputs 12 and 13), and he wants to combine the ride cymbal overhead microphone (input 11) on channels 9 and 10 as well. The ride cymbal channel is bussed to tracks 9 and 10 so the engineer can pan more signal to one track, and less to the other.

Each buss has a master trim, (an overall gain control used to lower the output level of each buss) sometimes called an attenuator, on its own channel. For example, the master trim for buss 25 appears on channel 25 on the desk. Because it is a trim, the master buss level goes *down* from 0db.

When two busses on a channel are pressed, the buss output level is the same on both. For example, if buss 25 is patched into a delay, and buss 26 is patched into an echo plate, pressing busses 25 and 26 on any channel would send the same signal level to both the delay and the echo plate. If you wanted the output of buss 25 lowered, you could use the master trim on channel 25. Note that this lowers all signals bussed to 25.

Though the input/setup sheet states that some busses to tape will need outboard patched into the signal, buss all channels to the multitrack machine first, then complete the patching.

THE PATCHBAY

The patchbay (also called a jackfield) centralizes all channel access points on the desk, plus all inputs and outputs of the outboard equipment in the control room. This lets the user bypass defective or unwanted components, add additional signal processing and re-route signal flow. As well, all inputs and outputs of all the recording machines are accessed at the patchbay.

Each patchbay is wired to suit each individual control room, so once you understand the patchbay, and how the normals are routed, you will have a good idea how all the equipment in the room integrates.

Although you will spend much of your time before, during, and after the session setting up equipment, an important part of your job is setting up, keeping track of, and breaking down the patchbay. (See Chapter Eight for more on patching.) Watching the patchbay can be very exciting. For now, here are some guidelines:

- Understand absolutely everything about the patchbay. Every patch point in the bay is there for a reason. Visualizing the signal flow helps in understanding how the engineer wants things patched. Think like an engineer.

- Always patch in the direction of signal flow. For example, to insert a limiter into a channel, patch out of the insert send on a channel, into the limiter, out of the limiter, back into the insert return. Insert returns are access patch points, either pre or post equalization, on each channel to allow additional processing, for example inserting a limiter to be patched into the signal.

- Leave a note pad by the patchbay to organize everything from writing down patches to taking lunch orders. I once asked the studio manager why I should keep a pad by the bay. He said, "It's nice to get away for the weekend."

- If possible, use similarly colored patchcords for similar functions, for example red cords for sends, green for returns. Use cables of the same lengths for stereo returns, not one long cable and one short cable.

- Use appropriate patchcords with good connectors at both ends. Sometimes patchcords lose their end casings, leaving the connecting wires are exposed. Remove these patch cords and get them repaired, as using them may yield unpredictable results. They also cut your finger when you push them into the patchbay.

- While making the patch, mute the returning channels on the desk to avoid a loud pop in the speakers, unless this will deaden an active microphone.

- When patching in stereo, always double check that the left stays left, and the right stays right.

- Some outboard equipment has an *in/out* switch on the faceplate (also called the front panel) that allows it to be deactivated while still in line. If there is an in/out switch, take the signal out and let the engineer activate it at his leisure.

- When testing equipment for input and output levels, patch out of the oscillator into the unit to see input on the meters. As the return of the unit is not yet patched, you will see the input to the unit, but not the return levels at the desk.

- There are various ways to tell if the return from the unit is working properly. Some boards have access to line input levels to meters. If this is the case, patch the return into the meters on the desk, and watch it react with the instrument being sent to it.

Some boards don't have access to line input meters, so again, the best way is to patch the return into a nearby cassette machine in input mode, and monitor through headphones. When you have your proper parameters and levels to and from the unit, continue with the rest of the patches.

MICROPHONE INPUTS

Now that all equipment is set up, each signal to and from the desk needs to be individually tested for correct flow. With all the different cables, patches and busses, some signals may get inadvertently misrouted. Turning up the gain on one channel may tell you a microphone is working, but not which one.

Bring in a runner to help test the microphones. Tell him not to scratch the head of the microphone, but to snap his fingers in front of it. Some studio owners feel that years of scratching the front of microphones gives them that *scratched* look. The runner should only scratch the head if many microphones are close together, or in an awkward position where snapping his fingers in front would be ineffective.

When the signal flow of each channel is tested, the inputs to the machine are not normally monitored. The multitrack machine returns are monitored so if there is any problem with the complete signal path from microphone to desk to multitrack machine, and back to the monitor section of the desk, it will be immediately noticed. Now begin testing the inputs.

1) With the desk in *microphone* mode, and multitrack machine in *sync* mode, turn the control room monitor gain all the way off. Condenser microphones need a +48 volt power source, called phantom power, supplied at the desk. Turn on the phantom power on any condenser microphone channels, and set the control room monitor gain at a moderate level.

2) Put all the applicable tracks in *record-ready*, and *auto-input* on the multitrack machine.

3) To check that you are monitoring the right source, bringing up a few faders and listen for any room noise. If you hear no activity in the studio, trace down why not. The desk or multitrack machine may be in the wrong operating mode, the amplifiers may be off, or you may have lost your hearing.

4) Start with input 1, the microphone on the bass amplifier. According to the input/setup sheet (fig. 2.1.), a Neumann U-47 with a cardioid polar pattern is in front of the bass amplifier, plugged into input 1, and bussed to track 2 on the multitrack machine.

5) Double check with the runner that any pads have been set on the microphones, according to the input/setup sheet.

6) As the runner snaps his fingers in front of the first microphone, bring up main fader on channel 1. As channel 1 is bussed to track 2 on the multitrack machine, look at the input meter 2 on the machine to see any input.

7) Bring up monitor fader 2 on the desk to hear the signal returning to the desk.

8) If any outboard is patched into the signal, check that it is working correctly, with no buzzes or hums. When you have confirmed the signal is working and routed correctly, move on to the next channel on the desk.

DIRECT INPUTS

Not all inputs to the desk are microphone inputs. The second input to the desk is a direct input from the direct box on the bass guitar. If an instrument is connected, the runner might tap a string, or if it is a keyboard, he might press a key for you to hear if it is working.

If the input is just a loose ¼" cable waiting for an instrument to be plugged in, the runner can hold the cable and tap the end of the jack, creating crackles and clicks on the input channel. This will be enough to tell if the signal is getting into the desk. Once the inputs have been checked, turn the channels off before the musician arrives and plugs in. Continue with the rest of the inputs, until all are working properly, or a problem is discovered.

CHASING, TRACING AND REPLACING

Often, for any number of reasons, you cannot hear the signal, so the problem needs to be traced. Have the runner speak into the microphone, or tap the line input, while you watch at the input meter on the multitrack machine. If you turn the monitor gain way up to make sure the signal is definitely not coming through, remember to lower it again. If you leave the monitor gain up, when the problem is discovered, the channel will come on very loud. To trace a signal that is not working:

- If you see signal reaching the machine, you know the problem is not with the microphone or the input section of the channel, but in the monitor section.

- If you see no signal getting to the multitrack, the problem is in the studio or at the input stage. Trace the problem by the process of elimination. Listen to the input of the channel where it enters the desk. If signal can't be heard, then the problem probably lies within the studio.

- Turn the channel off and have the runner trace the cables in the studio. The cable or microphone may need replacing.

- If the problem lies in the control room, check the desk and the patchbay. Is the phantom power on? Is the signal bussed and patched correctly? Is the channel in the right mode? Is everything turned on? Is anything blocking the signal at the patchbay? Eventually, you will find and fix the problem.

CUE SENDS

Often, as mentioned in the section on headphones, different sections of the band want their own mix of the song in their headphones. Most musicians want the same feel with headphones that they get during rehearsals. A drummer may want lots of bass, and very little guitars, while the guitarist may want lots of drums and no keyboards. To do this, the engineer may set up any number of independent cue sends. Desk limitations may dictate that some cue mixes be in mono, not stereo.

The cue mix also may be the actual monitor mix off the desk. When the engineer changes any levels or panning on his monitor mix, these changes also occur in the headphones. According to the input/setup sheet (fig. 2.1.), the drummer and bass player receive cue send 1, guitar player/singer 1, guitar player 2, and the keyboard player receive cue send 2. While the runner is speaking into a microphone in the studio, turn up the applicable cue sends. When the runner hears himself in the headphones, the cue is working properly.

MASTER SENDS AND RETURNS

Most desks have between four to eight sends on each channel. The center section contains the master cue send, and is used to change the overall send levels and sometimes equalization, depending on the individual desk. There is also a corresponding number of returns in the center section, usually stereo, used to return effects without tying up individual channels.

Don't turn the master cue send levels all the way up. If the cues don't appear loud enough, raise them on the individual cue boxes. During the session, if the musician wants more overall cue level, and the master send is all the way up, the individual level on each channel would have to be raised, changing the cue mix. It is more convenient for the engineer to simply turn up the overall mix, than each individual channel. Once the cue mix is set and correct, it shouldn't need changing.

TALKBACK

The talkback section of the desk has a built-in microphone that lets the people in the control room talk with the people in the studio. It is also used to slate each take. The engineer slates the take by speaking into the talkback microphone, and recording the song title and take number on tape before the song starts.

Many studios have some sort of remote button on the end of a long cable that, when pressed, activates the talkback microphone on the desk. The producer can just lean back in the control room, press the remote control button, and talk to the studio. Often he thinks that the remote he is holding is the actual microphone, much like a CB radio, and talks directly to it not realizing it's only the button that activates the microphone on the desk. This usually creates peals of laughter within the assistant engineer community, especially when no one tells him.

As with the master send levels, check the talkback level for proper output before the session begins. Better the level is too quiet than too loud. Here are a few guidelines when dealing with the talkback in session:

- When the talkback is on, keep quiet. Rustling papers and casual conversation in the background comes through loud and clear.

- Only talk through the talkback if you are engineering, or if you are talking to the engineer in the studio. It is not your place to make comments to the band through the talkback.

- Keep the engineer's headphones away from the talkback as they may feed back when the talkback button is pushed.

- When the engineer wants to talk to a musician one to one, he may press the control room monitor *cut* button, walk into the studio, and speak to a musician. Leave the control room monitor button cut. He obviously doesn't want the people in the control room to hear him.

TRACKSHEETS

Tracksheets are used to organize the track layout of every song or performance. Each song gets its own tracksheet. In the days of mono, there wasn't much need for tracksheets. As the recording industry evolved from one track to two, two to four, eight, sixteen, twenty-four, and so on, an accurate system of record keeping for each track on every song was needed. The information written on the individual tracks on the tracksheet is the same as the multitrack returns on the desk's monitor section.

Tracksheets are kept in one of two places: on or near the desk where the engineer can easily reach it, or, if not in use, in the box with the multitrack tape. Some engineers prefer to fill in the tracksheets themselves. Whoever fills them in, you are responsible for making sure all pertinent information for organization purposes is included. Figure 6.3. is a typical completed 24-track tracksheet. This tracksheet shows basic tracks and overdubs. This is *not* how all tracksheets are laid out; most studios use different styles of tracksheet. Everything written on the tracksheet must be accurate, legible, and current. An inaccurate or incomplete tracksheet will do more damage than good. The tracksheet is broken down into three major sections:

PROJECT INFORMATION

The project information is found at the top of the tracksheet. This section includes the song title, the artist or band, the producer, the engineer, the client, and the assistant engineer. The assistant's name is included so anyone else working on the tapes with questions or problems will know who to commend or yell at. And remember, nobody likes their name spelled incorrectly.

This section also indicates how the multitrack machine is set up, including the brand of tape, machine alignment reference levels, location of tones, track format (the number of tracks, usually 8, 16, 24, 32, or 48), tape speed, varispeed (if any), noise reduction (if any), and sometimes the beats per minute of the song; also, whether the tape is analog or digital, master or slave. You wouldn't normally log the alignment information on every tracksheet unless a special alignment was done for the individual song. Also included might be the studio used, such as studio A or studio B.

If the tracksheet is large enough to be folded in half, write the song title on the back of the sheet as well as the front. When there are five songs on a multitrack reel, there are five tracksheets in the tape box as well. Having the title written on the back of each sheet may save a few seconds rooting around in the box.

INDIVIDUAL TRACKS

Individual tracks are always written in pencil, as they may be modified, bounced, or simply erased. Log the track information *during* the recording, not before. Each track should contain:

- The instrument. Sometimes simply writing "keyboard" or "guitar" isn't enough. Write the complete name of the instrument, for example "Emulator 3 Grand Piano #2" or "'59 Fender Acoustic."

- The part. Write down the complete part, such as "high rhythm," or "low harmony 1." Additionally, notice in fig. 6.2. tracks 19 and 20 are in stereo, but tracks 15 and 17 are not, although they are the same part. Track 17 is labeled "with 15" and not "L" or "R."

- Internal location. As the tracksheet gets filled up, additional space may be needed. Often, a lack of available tracks dictates using one track for more than one instrument. The guitar on track 15 happens only in the intro and choruses of the song. This leaves space for additional recording during the verses. Notice on the tracksheet that a tambourine was recorded as an overdub on track 15.

- Musician. The musician's name is written down only if there is more than one person playing a similar instrument. As in labeling the scribble strip, three guitar players would each have their names written on the tracks they played. One saxophone player wouldn't.

(AEH)	TITLE: Too TUFF TO TAME
	ARTIST: TUFF BEANS
	PRODUCER: A JAFFEE
	ENGINEER: HERBIE HYNDE
	CLIENT: BLACK INK PUBLISHING

☐ 48 TK   ☐ 32 TK   ☒ 24 TK   ☐ 16 TK   ☐ 8 TK

1 TALKBACK	2 BASS GUITAR AMPLIFIER	3 BASS GUITAR DIRECT	4 KICK DRUM
DATE:	MIC:	DATE:	MIC: U·47	DATE:	MIC:	DATE:	MIC: 421
ENG:	STUDIO:	ENG:	STUDIO:	ENG:	STUDIO:	ENG:	STUDIO:

9 — CYMBALS — RIDE OVERHEAD	10	11 ROOM AMBIANCE	12
DATE:	MIC: U·87	DATE:	MIC: U·87	DATE:	MIC: 414	DATE:	MIC: 414
ENG:	STUDIO:	ENG:	STUDIO:	ENG:	STUDIO:	ENG:	STUDIO:

17 RHYTHM GUITAR '59 STRAT INTRO + CHORUSES DOUBLE OF 15 ACOUSTIC GUITAR O.D VERSES 7·30	18 LEAD VOCAL A	19 L	20 KEYBOARDS KORG → YAMAHA R
DATE:	MIC:	DATE:	MIC: U·87	DATE:	MIC: DI	DATE:	MIC: DI
ENG:	STUDIO:	ENG:	STUDIO:	ENG:	STUDIO:	ENG:	STUDIO:

Figure 6.3. Trackseet

- Date. Write the recording date of every overdub for cross referencing your setup sheets and daily log. If there is no date written on the individual track, it is a basic track, and hasn't been updated. Of course, if everything is recorded in one day, there is no need to write down the recording date for all overdubs.

DATE: JULY 29	TAPE: 696	SPEED: ☒ 30 IPS	☐ 15 IPS	☐ DIGITAL
STUDIO: ☒ A ☐ B ☐ C		N. R.: ☐ DOLBY	☐ DBX	☐ _____
REEL: 1 OF: 5		SAMPLING RATE: ☐ 48 K		☐ 44.1 K
TONES ON REEL __1__ ☐ HEAD ☒ TAIL		REF: 380 nWm = 0VU ☐ NAB		☐ IEC
ASSISTANT ENGINEER: A. READER				

☐ 4 TK   ☒ MASTER   ☐ SAFETY   ☐ SLAVE   ☐ CLONE

5 SNARE DRUM	6 HIGH HAT	7 TOM TOMS LOW MID	8 HIGH
DATE: MIC: 57/451	DATE: MIC: 451	DATE: MIC: 421	DATE: MIC: 421
ENG: STUDIO:	ENG: STUDIO:	ENG: STUDIO:	ENG: STUDIO:
13 VOCAL WORK TRACK #1 O/D	14 VOCAL WORK TRACK #2 O/D	15 GUITAR 1 '62 LES PAUL INTRO + CHORUSES DOUBLE OF 17 TAMBORINE O/D VERSES 1:30	16 GUITAR 2 TELECASTER
DATE: 7:30 MIC: U47	DATE: 7:30 MIC: U87	DATE: MIC: 421 · DI	DATE: MIC: 57
ENG: STUDIO:	ENG: STUDIO:	ENG: STUDIO:	ENG: STUDIO:
21	22 ACOUSTIC GUITAR O/D 2	23 CLICK 120 BPM	24 SMPTE TIMECODE 30 FPS
DATE: MIC:	DATE: 7:30 MIC: U87	DATE: MIC:	DATE: MIC:
ENG: STUDIO:	ENG: STUDIO:	ENG: STUDIO:	ENG: STUDIO:

- Origin. If the track is a fly-in or bounce from another track, note its origin, and the date of the bounce or fly-in. (See Chapter Ten for more on fly-ins.) Tracks are often bounced within a master, from master to slave, and from slave to master. If the track is not from the basic session, mark OD, for overdub, on it. Notice on the tracksheet which tracks are from the basic, and which are overdubs.

- Suggestions and reminders. Any ideas or reminders, such as specific panning or effects the engineer wants to remember for mixing are sometimes added. Some tracks may be kept strictly for reference, and are not meant for use in the final mix, such as the guide vocal on track 21. This track will probably be used until the final choice vocal track is completed, then labeled with DNU (do not use).

  Some tracks are recorded as work tracks, also called feeders, and used to make one choice compilation track. (See Chapter Ten for more on work tracks.) When a track is to be erased, it is labeled with TBE (to be erased.) *Check with the engineer before erasing anything.* Once the choice vocal track is established, mark it with a star using a red felt pen.

- Non-music tracks. Historically, the fidelity on edge tracks (tracks on the outer edge of the multitrack tape, such as track 1 and track 24) was not always as high as the fidelity on internal tracks. These tracks were used as non-program tracks, such as click, talkback, and timecode. Whenever timecode is recorded, write down the specific type, its starting time, and any offsets used. (See Chapter Ten for more on timecodes.)

CUE	TIME	CUE	TIME
INTRO	0	CHORUS 2	2:44
VERSE 1	:14	BRIDGE	3:23
B. SECTION	:37	SOLO	3:45
VERSE 2	:52	CHORUS 3	4:05
B. SECTION 2	1:18	" "	4:26
CHORUS 1	1:37	" "	4:40
VERSE 3	2:07	END	4:57

Figure 6.4. Song Cues

- Engineer and studio. When more than one engineer is used, write each engineer's name on the tracks they recorded. List other studios used as well.

- Signal information. The microphones, limiters, and equalizers used during recording are sometimes also noted, though this information will also appear on the setup sheet. (See Chapter Nine for more on setup sheets.)

CUES

Using the multitrack machine's counter numbers, write the basic structure of the song, commonly called the cues, on the tracksheet to help the engineer find where he is in a song or reel. These numbers start at the beginning of each song. As the song progresses, write down the counter numbers at every four or eight bars, or at specific changes within the song structure. Figure 6.4. Timecode numbers printed to tape are preferable, as they are more reliable than the machines counter.

. . . .

Summary

Chapter Six explained about understanding and setting up the desk and patchbay for the session:

- Understanding the normals within the studio and control room.

- Preparing the desk for the session, including zeroing the channels, writing out the strip, switching the desk to the correct operating mode, setting all the busses and completing all the pre-session patching.

- Going through each channel with a runner and testing all signal flow from the studio to the multitrack machine, then back to the desk.

- Setting the cue and master send levels.

- Preparing and filling in the tracksheets.

CHAPTER SEVEN

· ·

Session Priorities

Now that all the equipment is set up and the session is ready to go, here are a few guidelines to help you keep the session running smooth and efficient for everyone:

- Keep up with the engineer. Understand the complete signal flow of the session, including all patching, bussing, and signal routing. You can't tell if something isn't reacting correctly if you don't know or understand the signal path. If he tells you to do something that seems wrong, such as changing a tape half way through the reel, you can question it because you are right there with him. Get on his wavelength. The ideal situation is to know what he wants before he tells you.

- Keep the session rolling. Keep all changes fast and efficient. There is no time to chat while changing the tapes or setting up equipment. If someone asks you to do something, wait until the tapes and equipment are set up and the engineer has everything he needs to continue.

- If you don't know something, say you don't know. If you did something wrong, say you did something wrong. You and the engineer must be on the same team. This isn't like the medical profession, where you can fake it as you go.

- Set priorities for each situation. If the engineer wants a limiter in the vocal channel, a sandwich from the deli, a fire extinguisher, and details of studio scheduling, you need to re-arrange these in the order of priorities. You wouldn't leave the room to get a sandwich before making the patches, and it seems more important to put out the fire before asking the manager about studio availability.

- Continually scan the room to make sure everything is acting and reacting as it should, including the inputs to the machines, the meters on all the equipment, triggers on the samplers, the desk, the outboard, and even the musicians. Keep all doors closed, and listen for any fans or air conditioners that may be on. If you see or hear something wrong, tell the engineer before he presses the *record* button.

- Keep the engineer from recording over anything. When he puts a track in *record-ready,* check the tracksheet and make sure the proper signal is going to the proper track. This should become second nature. When he changes something on the desk, lean over his shoulder and double check that his change is correct. If he changes the signal path incorrectly, or busses something incorrectly, go over and quietly point it out. It's like looking after your grandfather — he can teach you a lot, but you always need to keep an eye on him.

- When there is a problem, don't let the session know. The clients should never know of any troubles or malfunctions. If a problem occurs, such as equipment not working, simply work around it without making a big deal. Either quietly tell the engineer, or slip him a note. Of course, urgent problems call for urgent actions. If he is recording over an important track, don't slip him a note telling him so.

- If the engineer makes a mistake, don't let the session know. The musicians and the producer must have faith in him, and you shouldn't undermine that. Don't make him look like an idiot in front of everyone. He can do that himself.

- Don't wait for the engineer to ask you to do things — just do them. If someone in the session asks the engineer to play a specific section of a song, find it before the engineer asks you. If you hear the engineer tell a musician he is going to put an equalizer on his instrument, don't wait for him to tell you, just make the patch. If he tells a musician to wait because a microphone needs changing, be out the door to change it. As well, if you know how the engineer likes certain equipment set up, do it without being asked. For example, if a vocal overdub is being started, and you know he always uses a specific equalizer and limiter in a certain order, set it up without him having to ask you.

- Watch the musicians to make sure they have everything they need to be comfortable and ready for the session. When anything needs changing, like headphones or cables, change them fast. Occasionally listen to the headphone mixes to hear if anything in the mix is unusually loud or quiet. If you hear something wrong, tell the engineer. Some musicians won't hear anything specific, they will just know something is not right in their headphones.

- Keep equipment turned on and ready to be used. When something is not working correctly, label it as out-of-order, and get the technical staff on it. Check all machines for proper input levels. Cassette machines should be loaded and ready to record.

- Do something good early in the project. This should earn you a goodly amount of trust throughout the rest of the project from the producer and engineer, enough perhaps for them to consider you for some minor engineering. This will also allow you some freedom with small mistakes. If they feel you are doing a great job, small mistakes will be forgotten. If they feel you are doing a poor job, the same small mistake becomes a large mistake.

- If you are working with an engineer you have never worked with before, after a few days, ask him how you are doing, and what you can do to help him more effectively. This will show him that you really care about doing the best job you possibly can.

- Stay in the control room. The engineer needs you to set up equipment, change routing, get coffee, answer any questions or address any problems. He doesn't want to have to hunt around for you when he needs a patch. You can't keep up with him if you are in the lobby playing video games.

- During an intimate vocal, a musician may become distracted with you moving around in the control room, or worse, staring at him while he sings. These are times when you dim the lights, settle into the darkness and quietly do your job.

- Don't change the settings on anything without the engineer knowing about it. If something doesn't seem right, mention it, and let him deal with it. During recording, he has many things to listen to. If any settings get changed, it may not be immediately realized. If you must make a change, for instance when the engineer is out of the room, mention it when he returns. Keep him up to date.

- Keep quiet. Your job is to assist the engineer, not to give your opinion. There is nothing much worse than an assistant who won't shut up. Of course, as you get more comfortable with a musician, producer and engineer you can feel out how casual to be. Take a second to think before asking any stupid questions.

- Don't start talking about other sessions. Something that happened last week in another session may seem funny to you, but the client doesn't want to hear it. He wants to concentrate on his project, not be interrupted with your so-called "humorous" little anecdotes.

- Keep the control room as quiet as possible. Only what the session is working on should be heard. Use headphones to trim up samples, set delay times, or find a section of tape. Turn off the channel when changing cables, patches, microphones or their settings, or anything involved with signal. Don't feed anything loud back into the monitors. Turn the monitors off when the machine is in rewind so the tape whizzing past the heads can't be heard. Keeping the control room quiet also means not yelling across the room to the engineer. Go over and speak to *him*, not to everyone in the control room.

- Get the client in and out on time. Give the engineer plenty of warning if another session is scheduled to start right after yours. But don't tell the musician, leave that to the engineer or producer. It can be a difficult situation when the next client is waiting to start, and the engineer wants a little more time to finish the mix. Of course, if you are working into the night, or if the sessions are locked out, being out on time may not be an issue. (A lock-out is when the client rents the studio full-time, 24 hours a day.)

- Stay awake. Don't even yawn (it's catchy.) The client should feel that you are in complete control, not about to doze off. This may sound funny, but when working long hours, falling asleep can easily happen. Having finished all your work, you must sit around the control room and watch everyone else work. There may be times when you gently slip into the arms of Morpheus.

- Don't sit around and read when there is work to do. It is alright if you are reading a manual, or researching something for the engineer, but in general, don't do it unless you have done absolutely everything else. The client may not have total faith in you if he sees you with your feet up on the desk reading an Archie comic.

- Don't treat any project casually. No one knows who the next major stars and producers will be, or where the next hit record comes from. You always want to do your best for the people you are working with.

- Don't go into the studio when something is being recorded. That magical take can happen at any time, and it will be unusable if you can be heard clomping around in the background. If you absolutely must go into the studio while recording, be as quiet as possible.

- Sit at the desk next to the engineer as often as you can. This will give you his sonic perspective, so when he makes a change you can hear what he is hearing. If he asks you to move, then move, but return when you can. Of course, if there is only one extra chair, the producer has rank.

- Avoid drugs and alcohol. To get ahead in the studio, you must be on the ball. It is important for everyone in the session to have full confidence in your abilities and the decisions you are expected to make. If you make a mistake under the influence, it will not be forgotten.

- Wear earplugs, even if no one else does. Don't let some deaf recording engineer blast you with loud volumes for hours on end. Use them at any sign of increased volumes, in the studio or out. In the good old days, the gauge of having a good time at a concert was directly related to the amount of ringing in your ears. "I had such a good time that my ears are still ringing, and the concert was last year." Your hearing is your livelihood, protect it.

THE TELEPHONE

Your job also involves answering the telephone. This may be the outside world calling in, or just elsewhere on the premises. Some studios have phone systems more complicated than the Concorde cockpit and invariably more difficult to master. However, every call is important, so learn how to use the studio's phone system.

Check ahead of time with the producer if any calls are to be held. Sometimes people in the session just can't take a call. They may be recording, having an important discussion, or simply not available, so use your best judgment. Write down the caller's name and number, who the call was for, and when it was received.

You should not take any personal calls while in session. If you must take an important call, take it somewhere out of the control room.

There will be times when you must judge whether someone wants to talk privately, like when the producer's girlfriend or wife calls — or when they both call. If you and he are the only ones in the room, leave so he can talk privately. Keep your eye on the control room phone line from another room to see when he is through, then return to the control room.

If a call comes in for someone in another studio, go in and tell the assistant on that session. Do not barge in and tell the whole room.

THE DOOR

Some studios have a little button to open the front door from the control room. Some may even have a video monitor to see who is at the door. In some studios, you are responsible for answering the door. Be careful who you let in, as you don't want to unknowingly open the door to a pack of overzealous fans to run rampant through the studios.

Never let anyone into the session without checking with the producer. Often, people from the outside world like to stop by and hang out during sessions. Sessions are closed unless you are told otherwise. Artists can become uncomfortable when there is a strange face in the control room. And this industry has some strange faces! If you are not working on the session — even if you know everyone there — keep out. No one is allowed into the session except the musicians, the producer, and the engineering staff (you, the engineer and sometimes a runner, who might sit in the corner to quietly watch and learn.)

WHEN THE COMPANY REPRESENTATIVES STOP BY

At some point during most larger budget record projects, the financial backers, such as representatives from the record company, may come by to hear how the project is going. This is the time the band is trying to get approval from the people putting up all the money.

When these people come by, don't make any jokes or comments about anything. Do the job, remain silent, and stay in the room. Make absolutely sure the place is clean and organized. A messy workplace will create a more anxious atmosphere, giving them the impression that the studio and staff (this means you) may not be up to par. Get everyone what they want, be it coffee, tea, soda, etc., then clean up the empty containers.

Before these people arrive, find out what song to play first. Cue the song up correctly, and play only what the producer wants them to hear. If you need to find the exact spot, use headphones so no one hears anything but the correct song. Play the complete song from the beginning to the end. If you are unsure of the choice take to play, quietly find out from the producer.

REFRESHMENTS

COFFEE AND TEA

Most people in the recording industry think the mainstay of being an assistant engineer is getting coffee or tea. Well, it is! Good coffee or tea flows through a studio, so get the studio manager to spring for the good stuff, and learn how to make it. Please follow directions.

Keep a supply of clean cups, spoons, and of course honey, sugar, and cream. Remember what everyone takes in their coffee or tea, and place the cup where no one will be electrocuted if it gets spilled. Find a small table to put next to the engineer for his cup. Never put a beverage on the desk, or any other electronic equipment. During long sessions, take it upon yourself to bring a fresh cup of coffee to a weary engineer.

Always use real cups, not styrofoam. You get styrofoam cups down at the "Ten Minit Car Lube." People want to feel like they are important clients in your studio. Additionally, styrofoam cups are not re-usable and often become ash trays half full of cold coffee. Dealing with real cups means also being a dishwasher. Welcome to the glamorous world of recording!

ORDERING OUT

When people in the session need to order food, you will do all the organizing. Keep a collection of menus from neighborhood delis and restaurants. When everyone decides what they want to order, write the items down clearly, with how much money each person gave you. Place the order from the lobby, not the control room. Hopefully there will be a receptionist or a runner to deal with food orders.

If no one else is available, you may be elected to run out to get the order. Always get a receipt. Before leaving the studio, clear it with the engineer. He may need you to set something up before you leave. Ask him to watch the telephone and the door when you are gone. However, most independent engineers won't feel obliged to answer your phone.

If the food is being delivered, check that the order is correct and complete before the delivery person leaves. No one wants a tongue and liver sandwich when they ordered a chef's salad. Get correct change for everyone and remember, if you want good reliable service from most delis, you have to tip.

Also, never let the delivery person into the control room. This is a private session where creativity must be allowed to run free. It can't really run free with Bubba, the delivery boy standing there waiting to get paid. Large budget sessions sometimes let dinner orders go on the work order, leaving the record company responsible for payment.

EATING YOUR LUNCH

Your job rarely entails a lunch break. If the band doesn't stop to eat, then neither do you. If you must eat, slip out of the room during a break. If there is work to do, you'll simply have to wait to eat your lunch. Do not eat your lunch in front of everyone. Nothing is more distracting than someone eating a limburger cheese and onion sandwich next to a musician who is trying to concentrate on a part.

I don't want to sound like your mother, but wash your hands after lunch. Handling tapes, tracksheets or equipment with greasy fingers isn't the greatest idea.

When everyone stops to eat, they often leave the studio entirely and enjoy their meal in the control room or the lobby. This can be a great time mid-session to do a quick studio cleanup. Of course, this translates into your dinner getting cold, while everyone else enjoys a hot meal. You will also clean up after everyone has finished eating. No one can be expected to be creative amongst leftover fast food wrappers. During jingle sessions, if the client is Burger King, don't eat a Big Mac.

DOWN TIME

Down time occurs when the session is unable to proceed due to malfunctioning equipment. When this happens, the clock is stopped and the technical staff is called in to solve the problem. When minor breakdowns occur, the offending equipment is either removed or bypassed at the patchbay with a minimum of fanfare. Don't let the client know about any minor technical difficulties if the difficulties don't affect the outcome of the session. Of course, if the control room is flooded with two feet of water, the client may clue in. When something directly affecting the session occurs, such checking the alignment, changing speakers, or a power outage, the clock is stopped while changes are made.

If power goes down, first mute the monitors. If the power goes out unexpectedly, it can come on just as unexpectedly. The amplifiers and machines powering up again with the monitors on would create quite a loud speaker-blowing pop. Second, unwind both sides of the tape on the machine to get it out of the sensor paths and away from the heads, then turn the multitrack machine off. If tape is left on the heads when the power is restored, the power spike may stretch the tape or create a click on the tape where it touches the heads. Many electronic devices tend to lose their set programs when powered down unless the settings have been stored in the internal memory.

When legitimate down time occurs, state aloud the time, and that the session is now on down time. Keep exact records of when the down time began, and when the session started working again. The client will invariably question the length of down time written on the work order.

Clients may see how this down time thing works, and try to shave some time off of their bill. They may say that setting up the equipment should be classed as down time, so the total hours billed should be lowered. They might spend too much time working out a part, or talking on the phone during session, then try to pressure the assistant to pass this off as down time on the work order. As some studios pay the assistants for the time billed to the client, this may mean that you wouldn't get paid for down time. Why should you not make any money while the musicians, producer, and engineer are probably rich enough combined to buy the Taj Mahal?

WHEN THINGS GO WORNG

When I was starting out as an assistant engineer, I accidentally spilled a full can of soda into the main faders on the new desk. I panicked and ran around trying to figure out how to turn the desk off before it exploded. Later the engineer chastised me, not for spilling the soda into the desk, but for showing my lack of ability to handle a crisis in front of the client. Of course, the session was called off while the cleanup took place. (The studio manager later asked me what I was going to do about this situation. I said I'd probably just buy another soda.) The lesson here is, before going into the studio, know what the procedures are in case of emergencies. Hopefully you will never need to use them, but know exactly where the first aid kit, the fire extinguishers, and all fire exits are.

GETTING TECHNICAL

TECHNICAL STAFF

Most recording studios have a qualified technical staff to do all the equipment repairs, upgrades and alignments. They are the behind the scenes workers of the studio that keep the seeming endless array of new, used, ancient, and obsolete equipment operating. Depending on the size of the studio, the technical department might range from someone coming in occasionally to do repairs and check alignments, to a full crew 24 hours a day. Without a good technical staff, the recording studio would soon grind to a rusty halt.

If you really want to understand the workings of equipment in the studio, hang out when the technical staff is doing repairs. Usually, they are happy to explain things if you offer to lend a hand hauling equipment for them. But don't do their job unless you are expected to. The technical staff usually does not want you stepping on their toes by doing things like changing modules, or reseating cards. When dealing with the technical staff, remember one very important point. Many of them are "½ db off bias," if you know what I mean. If they like you, they can help you. If they don't like you, they can seriously hurt you. Go out of your way to stay on their good side.

In smaller studios the assistants are often required to help with some if the minor repairs. This may involve soldering wires for cables and headphones, doing the alignments, tracing any malfunctions, hauling and connecting equipment, and sometimes even doing a bit of carpentry. For major repairs or upgrades, equipment is either sent out, or a qualified technical person is brought in.

Helping the technical staff offers you the chance to delve deep into the workings of the studio. Understanding the electronics and signal flow of the studio gives you a major advantage over someone who doesn't have any electronics experience.

However, the technical side the studio is a bottomless pit. If you are the only employee with a grasp of repairing and upgrading electronic equipment, guess who will be doing all the studio repairs? This leaves little or no time to be an assistant.

THE SHOP

The technical room, also called the tech. room, or shop, is where most of the equipment gets tested and repaired. The shop contains all the equipment necessary to keep a studio operational — repair tools, equipment manuals, test equipment, and a nudie calendar. The shop is a good place to hang out and learn, but there are a few important guidelines:

- If you don't have direct permission to take things from the shop, don't. The shop is not normally your work area, it is someone else's.

- When you take or use anything from the shop, replace it where you got it, or your access to the shop may be restricted.

- Read the equipment manuals to understand how everything works. However, the best way to learn the operations of equipment in the control room is still the old fashioned way. Get in there and experiment.

MAINTENANCE REPORT NO. 130785	DATE: _July 29_
SESSION: _Tuff Beans_	TIME: _6 PM_
ENGINEER: _Herbie Hynde_	STUDIO:
ASSISTANT: _A. Reader_	☒ A ☐ B ☐ C

SYMPTOMS PLEASE BE EXPLICIT - INCLUDE ENVIRONMENT OF PROBLEM

Loud Hum in Left Side of Echo Chamber #1

TEMPORARY ACTION TAKEN:

Used Echo Chamber #2

REPAIRED BY: _____ DATE: _____

DIAGNOSIS:

PARTS SENT OR ORDERED: _____ DATE: _____

PARTS RECEIVED: _____ DATE: _____

Figure 7.1. Maintenance Form

- There may be things taken apart in there, so don't go poking around where you don't belong — for instance feeling how smooth and flexible the diaphragm on a disassembled microphone is. Speaking of microphones, don't take a microphone apart. Repairing headphones or cables is one thing, but not microphones. The insides are delicate, and they should only be disassembled by qualified personnel.

- Don't attempt to fix studio equipment unless you are authorized and totally confident that you can correctly complete the repairs. Most electronic equipment is easy to take apart but not so easy to re-assemble. Remember what happened to your first tape recorder?

MAINTENANCE FORMS

When equipment in the studio is not working properly, a maintenance form (also called a trouble sheet) is completed describing the malfunction. Figure 7.1. A problem described on the maintenance form usually isn't drastic enough to stop the session, but enough to warrant the technical staff's attention after the session ends.

Make the maintenance form as explicit as possible, stating the exact problem, how the signal was patched, the studio, the date, the engineer, the assistant, the time the problem was discovered and any temporary action taken. For example, the engineer notices a hum on the left return of an echo plate. Rather than stop the session to trace down the problem, he has you change the patch to another echo plate, and continues on with the session. The maintenance form is filled out explaining the situation, and the temporary action taken. It is then handed in with the work order after the session. The problem will, you hope, be taken care of before your next session.

Maintenance forms are numbered so all repairs can be correctly logged, with an explanation of who did the repairs, and what exactly was done. If the problem remains, you can go back to the original form and see what, if anything, was done to repair it. Sometimes just getting someone from the technical staff to have a quick look at malfunctioning equipment may resolve the problem. If the problem cannot be immediately repaired, the unit may have to be removed.

DAILY LOG

Write all information pertinent to the sessions in a daily log. Figure 7.2. This is a running schedule of what happened at what time throughout the session. The log can be a loose leaf book with removable pages, or just a pad of paper. Whatever system you use to log your daily information, it must be kept organized. A three-ring binder works best, as the pages are removable.

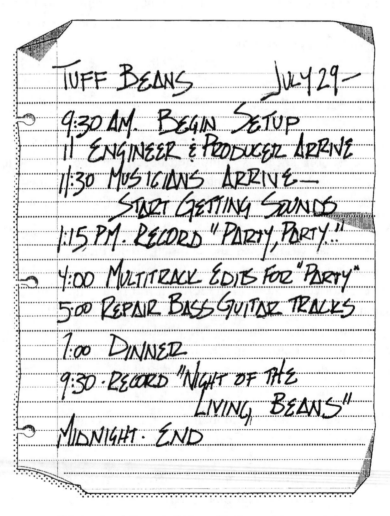

Figure 7.2. Page from the Daily Log

The main purpose of a daily log is to keep all information about sessions and equipment together and organized. Sometimes, when a track is recorded during basics, repaired weeks later, bounced to another track, etc., it may be quite a challenge to trace down any needed information. Any questions about any track must be traceable back through the paper trail.

Copies of setup sheets, lyrics, work orders (optional), maintenance forms, serial numbers for rental equipment, reminders to yourself, and the general day-to-day happenings should all be stored here and organized by time and date.

Also in the log is an up-to-date list of what is on all tapes, including master tapes, outtake reels, edit reels, rough mixes, and important DATs. If anyone wants to find any information about anything on tape, all information is right in your log. Anyone in the session can look through the log and easily find all information. I once worked on a project that had over 300 multitrack tapes. The daily log was more like a set of Funk and Wagnalls encyclopedias.

Be very careful about conflicting information. Something written on a setup sheet must not conflict with similar information in the daily log. Redundancy is the major cause of redundancy. Of course, this sort of organization is great but often, there simply won't be enough time or tapes to warrant listing all reels in the daily log.

INVENTORY SHEETS

Inventory sheets are used to keep track of incoming items in the studio. Figure 7.3. Multitrack tape, cassettes, DATs and other small items used in the session that are charged to the client can all be organized with a simple coding system.

For example, multitrack tapes might be labeled "M," cassettes might be "C," and DATs might be "D." Two boxes of 12 cassettes each would be individually labeled from "C-1" to "C-12," then "C-13" to "C-24." When any item assigned this number gets removed from storage, the number is written on the inventory sheet, and the work order for the individual session. Management then cross-references these to keep track of each client's charges. These items are generally kept in or near the tape vault, with stationery supplies and other studio goods, like splicing tape, leader tape, razors, alcohol, cottons swabs, etc.

INVENTORY SHEET		SESSION					TUFF BEANS.	

STUDIO	DATE	2"	1/2"	1/4"	DIG. 1	DIG. 2	CASSETTES	DATS
		M	H	Q	A	B	C	D
A	7.29	3		2			5	2
A	7.30	2						
A	7.31	3					1	
A	8.1	3	1	2				
B	8.2		4					
B	8.3		6				5	2
C	8.4						7	4

Figure 7.3. Inventory Sheet

MISTAKES

Before getting started with the sessions, a few words about mistakes in the studio. Even the best assistants and engineers have made mistakes. It is unrealistic to assume you will never make a mistake on your job. If you never have, you aren't working hard enough. Some mistakes, only you and the engineer know about. Some mistakes, everyone in the session knows about, and a few mistakes the whole recording industry hears about.

There are a few classic assistant engineer mistake stories, like the Steely Dan story. They allegedly worked on a tape for over a year, and the assistant who was recording the multitrack safety master totally erased the master tape by mistake. According to legend, after realizing his error, he put on his coat and casually walked off into the night, never to return. No one has seen him since.

There's the KISS story of when the new assistant stepped on, and snapped, the neck of Ace's rarest guitar. And the Bon Jovi story about the guy who turned the tape over to record a guitar track backward, and erased almost the whole keyboard intro of . . . wait a minute, that was me!

The point is, mistakes happen in all jobs. If you erase something important, it can be a blow to your self confidence, and to the confidence of the client. Again, whenever you make a mistake, tell the engineer. You and the engineer are on the same team, and in this together.

No matter what happens, remain calm and collected, and don't lose your cool in a crisis situation. You may do more harm than good, and you don't want the client to see your inexperience. Everyone needs to feel that you are really in control and know what you are doing. Minor mistakes are usually forgotten, but major mistakes are remembered, and tend to stay with you. If you accidentally burn down the studio, the engineer may be hesitant to use you on his next project.

. . . .

Summary

Chapter Seven explained about priorities before, during and after the session:

- Answering the phone, the door and getting refreshments in the studio, including coffee, tea, and ordering out.

- Down time procedures and recommendations. Dealing with the technical staff, and accessing the maintenance shop.

- Additional paperwork, including maintenance forms and the daily log.

- Mistakes in the studio. Everyone makes them.

CHAPTER EIGHT

. . . .

Recording Basic Tracks

The first, or primary tracks recorded are called basic tracks, over which overdubs are recorded. There is really no rule determining how a master basic track is established. Depending on the project, the budget, the studio, the band, and many other factors, a song may be recorded one time, or it may be recorded twenty times. The recording may be a single instrument, or a small combo, or a full band. The producer may choose one of the twenty, or the engineer might edit together the best sections of all the versions recorded. Once the basic track is established, overdubs may or may not be recorded. Does this clear things up? However the basic tracks are established, there are a few standard procedures during the recording of basic tracks.

MAKING CHANGES

The engineer should arrive for the session at least a half hour before the session starts. This allows for time to make sure everything is set up correctly. In the studio, he will adjust the microphones to exactly where he wants them. In the control room, he will go through each channel and check that all signals are correctly routed.

In the recording studio, change is inevitable. (It's usually behind the cushions in the cracks of the sofa.) Although the information from the input sheet may have been initially correct, the engineer will most likely want to make changes to suit the specific needs of the session. This may involve changing or adding microphones, cables, headphones, and patches until he is satisfied with all the sounds.

Murphy's Law dictates that at least one signal that worked perfectly before the session will mysteriously vanish when the engineer listens. It's usually something simple, like a wrong button pressed. Don't stand there saying, "Well, it was working before," as if this is the engineer's problem. His problem is your problem. Track down why he isn't hearing what he wants to hear.

While you are tracing and changing signals for the engineer, the rest of the people involved in the session may be arriving. As they do, help them with their equipment, their coats, their egos, and their spot in the studio.

If the musicians are new to the engineer, write each person's name and instrument on a small piece of paper, and put it on or near the desk for the engineer to see. Then the engineer doesn't have to refer to the drummer as "Hey Bignose."

CHANGING MICROPHONES

As the engineer works on the sounds to be recorded, he may not like the sound of a microphone, or a microphone may be faulty. To change the microphone for the engineer, follow this routine:

1) Before leaving the room to change a microphone, turn off the appropriate channel on the desk.

2) Go to the microphone room and find the replacement microphone. Then bring it into the studio.

3) Before unplugging the cable from the offending microphone, double check with the engineer that the correct channel has been turned off. Use the old "finger slice across the throat" routine to him to confirm the channel on the desk is cut. If he doesn't understand this universal gesture, give him another universal gesture he will understand.

4) Unplug the cable and remove the microphone with the shock mount, and set that microphone down on a soft surface.

5) Match the parameters from the original microphone to the new one.

6) Attach the new microphone to the stand, taking care to leave the placement in-tact; then connect the cable.

7) Signal for the engineer to turn on the channel and confirm that the replacement microphone is working.

8) Return the original microphone to the storage area or, if it is faulty, fill out a maintenance form and take the microphone to the shop.

Changing Microphone Parameters

When only the microphone's parameters need changing, again, have the engineer turn the appropriate channel off. If you are introducing a pad to the signal, you may need to either flip a switch on the microphone to activate it, install the pad between the microphone head and casing, or connect the pad where the XLR cable merges with the microphone. Keep the initial microphone placement the same, and gently make the change. Polar pattern changes are usually right on the microphone or, as with tube microphones, on the external power supply. Mark any changes on the setup sheet.

Final Microphone Placement

Just placing a microphone in front of an instrument or amplifier might not be exact enough for some engineers. An engineer may want you to slowly move the microphone around the instrument or amplifier while the musician plays. The engineer will listen in the control room, and signal to you to stop moving the microphone when he hears the elusive sweet spot, which is the place where he feels it sounds best. Stop moving the microphone, and tighten the stand, leaving the placement intact. Even the slightest movement may change the sound. Before placing a microphone in front of a loud amplifier, read the section on earplugs.

After the microphones are correctly placed and checked for signal flow, close the isolation booth, if one is being used. If necessary, throw a blanket or two over the booth for added isolation.

CHANGING CABLES

If the engineer tells you to change a cable because signal is not coming through as it should, glance over the signal path in the control room to see if a wrong button is pressed, a fader is down, or a patch is misrouted. If all seems well on the desk, then go out to the studio and replace the cable. Before doing so, again, remind the engineer to mute the channel. After replacing the faulty cable, tie a knot in one end and lay it aside so that it won't be re-used. If the signal still doesn't come through, the original cable was probably never faulty. The problem is elsewhere in the signal chain.

CHANGING HEADPHONES

When anyone says their headphones need changing, immediately be out the door to do the job. Follow these steps:

1) Get the headphones from the musician, then listen to them to hear the problem. Check that they are plugged in correctly, and that the headphone box is functioning properly. Test the headphones by plugging them into a nearby headphone box. If they are faulty, quickly exchange them.

2) After connecting the new headphones, listen to them before handing them to a musician. Don't change the cue level on the headphone box.

3) If, after the headphone change, the problem remains, replace the whole setup including headphones, cables, and headphone box. Match the levels on the replacement box with the one being removed. This is not the time to try to figure out the problem. Do whatever it takes to keep the session moving.

4) If you have the time after removing the faulty headphones, wrap a piece of adhesive tape around the side that does not work, and set them aside. Fill out a maintenance form, and take the headphones to the shop when convenient.

CHANGING PATCHES

Patches are changed throughout the session, from before the engineer arrives, to after he leaves. Most of your time is spent near the patchbay. Encourage the engineer to let you do all the patches, so you can keep up with the total signal flow. Here are a few guidelines:

- Keep the patchbay organized and up to date so the engineer can glance over and see how everything is routed. Remove any patches no longer in use after verifying that they are no longer needed.

- After you make a patch, double and triple check that the patch is working correctly. Any outboard equipment being patched must be turned on and set at a reasonable operating level. The engineer should never have to say "Hey, this is wrong." Trace the signal and make sure the flow is correct.

  For example, the engineer asks you to patch in a digital reverb. Make the patches, then go to the desk, turn up the send on a channel and look over at the input levels on the reverb. If the levels are good, turn up the returns on the desk for a split second. Not loud enough or long enough to distract the engineer, but enough to hear if the returns are working. If the setup is correct, leave the send and returns off until the engineer needs them. He won't want to hear the additional hiss from any effects returns that he isn't using.

- Don't root around in the patchbay while any machine is in *record*. Dirty patch cord connections may create crackles on tape. Wait until the multitrack machine is out of *record* to make a quick patch change.

  If you patch out of a channel while it is being recorded, the output patch sometimes loads down the input, which may lower the signal level to tape.

- As I mentioned earlier, always patch in the direction of the signal flow. For example, to patch a limiter and equalizer across a channel insert, patch from the channel insert send into the input of the limiter, then out of the limiter and into the input of the equalizer, then finally back into the channel insert return.

Because inputs in the patchbay are full normal, patching into the input of the channel first just creates a deadpatch. This channel is then silent until the rest of the patch is complete. If you follow the signal flow, the patch returning into the channel interrupts the signal not with dead space, but with the equalized signal.

- Make sure all patches will work. For example, the engineer wants to send the snare channel to an echo plate, using buss 12 as the send. Notice the bussing on the input/setup sheet (fig. 2.1.). Any channel bussed to track 12 will of course be recorded on track 12, which is one of the ambiance tracks. Tell him this, and mention that buss 13 is available. Make the patch and, to avoid recording the snare drum on track 13, take the machine out of *record-ready* on track 13, or deadpatch input 13 to the multitrack at the patchbay.

- After the patch is complete, give the engineer a slight confirmation, with maybe a nod. Go over to the unit you patched in and, using a piece of white adhesive tape, label it, stating the send and return. If he hasn't done so, write it on the strip clearly and legibly. Write the strip how he writes it. For example, if he uses red and blue markers, then you do the same.

- If the engineer writes something on the strip, such as sends and returns, don't wait until he asks you to make the patches. Read what he writes, and make them.

- After working with the engineer you will get to know how he uses certain pieces of equipment. If you have think you know where he is going with something, try to set it up. Don't make the patch and walk away. For example, if he labels stereo return 4 with "send 4 into delay unit 3, then into echo plate 4," you should realize what his intention is without him telling you. He probably wants a pre-delay on echo plate 4. Check that the delay unit is on and the gain isn't excessively loud before making the patch. Remove the feedback, and set the length of the delay approximately.

- When the engineer makes a patch, go over and look at it, double checking to see if he made the patch correctly. When necessary, as in mixing, write the patch down to keep track of the sound. If you feel he patched something incorrectly or you don't understand a patch that he made, ask him at an opportune time.

RECORDING THE BASIC TRACKS

Now everything is ready to go. The equipment setup and signal flow is complete, the musicians are comfortable and ready to play, and the engineer and producer are satisfied with the sounds. As the recording begins, scan the rooms to make sure everything is as it should be, including all meters on the multitrack machines, bussing, sends and returns, outboard equipment, and all input and output levels.

KEEPING TRACK OF CUES

Try to get the lyrics and/or sheet music for each song being recorded. The engineer might want to use these as a guide to help him become more familiar with the song as he hears it. When you get the final version of any lyrics, photocopy the page, and keep a copy in the log. Don't use a three-hole punch on original lyrics, only the copies. Date all lyrics to organize updated versions.

If possible, as each song is being recorded, write down the cues of the song on a separate page. When anyone wants to hear, for example, the first chorus of take 6, you can go directly to it, without having to wade through the whole song looking for a specific location. Keeping track of where a chorus, or a verse, or a bridge can be especially difficult if there is no vocal track recorded. After hearing the song a few times, you will generally get a feel for its structure. Once the choice version is established, write the master cue counter numbers on the tracksheet (fig. 6.3.).

Sheet music is mainly used when recording jingles, ensembles, and of course, orchestrations. It's not commonly used in pop or rock and roll. If your session is using sheet music, during the mayhem of recording, try to read along with the music and the cues. The ability to read music is an asset for a recording engineer.

RUNNING THE MACHINES

Traditionally, tape machines had no remote controls so the assistant sat in the corner and operated the machines all session. Today, with machine remotes near, or even within the desk, it is more convenient for the engineer to operate them. Some engineers still expect the assistant to do all the recording, including punch-ins (going in and out of *record* at exact spots.) Whoever is running the machines, your job is to:

- Make sure all multitrack machines are correctly loaded and ready to record. As the musicians run through the song to get the feel of it, most engineers will want to record this first pass. Less experienced musicians may be more relaxed during the run through if they think the tapes aren't running. In my experience, this first pass is sometimes the best.

- Make sure the tape is parked at the correct spot, and not on a section meant to be kept. If anything is erased, it's your fault. Many mistakes in the studio can be repaired, but once something not backed-up is erased, it's gone.

- When the tape is rolling, and the music is being recorded, watch the meters on the desk, the multitrack machine, and any limiters and compressors. As musicians get into a song, they may play their instruments harder than when they played for the sound check. If any meters are hitting the red, mention it to the engineer. Some engineers like to record very hot saturated levels to analog tape. Of course, digital tape can't be saturated, or the signal will give you pure distortion.

- Look at each track on the multitrack machine and check that the correct signal is being recorded on the intended track. For example, if you see a continuous tone-like signal going to the snare drum track, you know that the snare is not the only instrument being recorded on that track. Use you ears to hear the various instruments as you watch the meters on the machine.

- While recording, don't stop the machine until the engineer tells you to. You don't want to be guilty of pressing the *stop* button during a very quiet part in the middle of a song, or before the final chord of a song has finished ringing out. Of course, if there is something important about to be recorded over, say so.

- When the reel is not in motion, place sticky round dots (available at any stationery store) or a small piece of splicing tape on the analog tape to mark the takes. This is a fast and efficient method, used when the machine is in *rewind,* to pinpoint precise locations as each flag goes by. However, some engineers may not want the multitrack tapes peppered with sticky dots.

- For a temporary flag, slip a small bit of paper into the reel as the tape glides by, much like a bookmark sticking up between pages of a book. Of course, you lose your flag as soon as the reel is rewound past the spot. Between flags and counter numbers, everything on the reel should be easy to find. Some machines have instant locate memory buttons. Once pressed, any location is stored and recalled at the press of a button.

- Don't leave any tracks in *record-ready* if they aren't intended for immediate recording. If the engineer looks over and sees a tape machine in *record-ready* and loaded with tape, he may accidentally record over yesterday's choice take. Any machine in *record-ready* is fair game.

- Never let the tape run out while recording. If you aren't sure that there is enough room left on the tape for a complete take, change tapes before starting another take. The engineer will understand having to wait an extra minute or two while you change tapes. He won't understand losing the end of a fantastic take because the tape ran out.

- Unless there is plenty of time, don't install leaders during the recordings. Musicians often finish one take, and want to go directly into another. They shouldn't have to wait while you insert a leader between takes. Always check with the engineer before splicing tape. (See Chapter Nine for more on leadering.)

- Keep a cassette or DAT machine loaded and ready to record. Bands tend to jam, kid around, rehearse, and come up with new ideas between takes. These ideas may not be important enough to record to multitrack, but important enough to be kept. With a cassette or DAT machine cued up, these spontaneous ideas and meanderings can be instantly recorded. There may be little time to hunt for cassettes and to set levels when creativity hits.

Figure 8.1. Splice In Leader

- Leave some space (at least 30 seconds) between the passes on the tape. If the band records three passes in a row, then they want to record over the second pass, there should be ample space between songs so there is no chance of recording into the third pass.

- Double check with the engineer before recording over any previous passes. You don't want to accidentally record over a keeper due to a lack of communication.

- When you want to be extra sure not to record into the intro of the next pass, install a section of leader tape between takes. Then cut a small section, about one inch long and half an inch high off the bottom of the leader tape. Figure 8.1. As the opening goes by the machine's electric eye, the circuit closes and disables the transport system, automatically stopping the machine. Of course, to do this it must have an electric eye. Wouldn't it be great if the machine had an electric nose, too? Then it would just erase the stuff that really stinks.

TAKESHEETS

Takesheets are used to organize recorded performances, whether complete or incomplete, and for any specific comments by the producer. Figure 8.2. The machine's counter numbers are written down so you can find any specific section. Each time a take is recorded the engineer slates the tape with a number and uses this number for reference. Without this reference number, locating specific takes on tape would be a nightmare.

Tracksheets and takesheets and are similar, yet their functions are very different. Tracksheets are used to log the track layout within a song, and takesheets are used to log the takes within a tape. When not in use, keep takesheets in the box with the tape.

Keeping up with all the necessary paperwork can be a big task. Sessions rely on the assistant to log all information correctly. Everything must be clear and legible, so that finding any track, song, or tape is quick and easy. The takesheet is broken down to two basic sections: project information, and titles and locations.

PROJECT INFORMATION

This section is filled in the same way as the tracksheets. As takes can sometimes be fast and frequent during recording, writing all the project information on each takesheet can be time consuming. Unless a special alignment or setup was done for a particular take, this information is probably not needed on every takesheet. More important is the reel number, each take number, its corresponding counter number, date, producer, engineer, and assistant engineer.

TITLES AND LOCATIONS

During the session, writing down the takes and their locations has priority over almost everything else, except perhaps filling in the tracksheets. A lot of time can be lost trying to make up for poor or incorrect record keeping. This section includes:

- Titles. It's pretty obvious what goes here: the name of the song or musical passage being worked on.

- Take. This shows the number of the take. Often, incomplete or unsatisfactory takes are recorded over with new takes, then assigned new numbers. Notice take 5 was replaced with take 6. Slate numbers must be consistent. If a take is slated with a wrong number, such as take 2 being called take 3, either tell the engineer and he will slate the take again, or add a clear explanation on the takesheet. A lot of time and energy may be wasted later hunting around for a nonexistent take 2.

DATE: JULY 29 REEL: 6 OF:	☑30 IPS ☐ 15 IPS ☐DIG.
ARTIST: TUFF BEANS	REFERENCE:_____ nWm = 0VU
PRODUCER: D. MARTIN	☐ 1K ☐ THIS REEL
ENGINEER: HERBIE HYNDS,	☐ 10K ☐ REEL#_____
ASSISTANT: A. READER	☐ 15K ☐ RECORD PAD
	☐ 50 Hz ☐ HEAD ☐ TAIL
CLIENT:	☐ 100 Hz ☐ N. R._____

☐MASTER ☐ COPY
☐SAFETY ☐ CLONE

☐ 48TK ☐ 32TK ☒ 24TK ☐ 16TK ☐ 8TK ☐ 2TK

TITLES		TAKE	LOCATE / CTL	TIME	COMMENTS
NIGHT OF THE LIVING BEANS		3	0		FS.
''	''	4	1:10		C GOOD CHORUS
''	''	6	5:30		INC.
''	''	7	6:30		C ALTERNATE INTRO
''	''	8	11:00		

FS - FALSE START	C - COMPLETE	HL - HEAD LEADER	TL - TAIL LEADER	HTL - HEAD AND TAIL LEADER
INC - INCOMPLETE	H - HOLD	HM - HEAD MARK	TM - TAIL MARK	HTM - HEAD AND TAIL MARK

Figure 8.2. Takesheet

- Locate/CTL The counter on the tape machine is used to find specific locations on the reel. As well, the counter is used to gauge tape and time left on the reel. For example, at 30 ips (inches per second) a standard analog multitrack reel should last for a bit longer than 16 minutes. According to the takesheet sheet, a complete pass of the song takes about 4 minutes. If the tape is parked at 11 minutes, you know there is enough space on the reel for one more complete pass.

When using digital tape, you must pre-format the tapes by recording a control code (absolute time, also called A-time) before the session. This code does not take up one of your program tracks — it records on its own internal code track. This code always lets you see exactly where you are on the tape without having to set the start time.

- Time. This section shows how long each song is. The numbers showing where a take starts and stops may not reveal a song's exact time. The tapes might roll for a few moments before the song actually starts, or an intro may be planned for later recording during an overdub.

- Comments. The comments section shows the status of each numbered take using the codes at the bottom of the takesheet. An FS label means a false start, INC means incomplete, C means a complete take. When the passes are leadered, they are marked with HTL, head and tail leadered. Other abbreviations not on this takesheet are: ALT, an alternate version, and CHOICE, a take that will be used.

There are many more options, but these few tend to be used most. Additionally, general comments by the producer or engineer, like "good choruses" or "great ending" are written here to help everyone remember the best parts. Mark these comments down even if they aren't speaking directly to you, such as when the producer tells the engineer about a take or section of a take he prefers.

LABELS

With tapes properly labeled, everyone's job is much easier. Every tape must be clearly marked with exactly what is on it, and be consistent with the rest of the tapes. Sessions can go through many reels of multitrack tape, continually recording and keeping all takes until all choice sections are recorded. All tapes need to be labeled with the basic session information. As with the tracksheet, write all names, titles and project information clearly and precisely.

Writing out a few multitrack labels beforehand will save time during the session, when changing tapes is fast and furious. When a virgin tape is loaded, apply a pre-written label. During the session, all that needs to be added is the tape number, song titles and locations, and any notes or comments. As digital tape lasts much longer per reel than analog tape, pre-labeling may not be necessary.

Figure 8.3. shows a typical tape label. It can be used for all tapes, including master tapes, slave tapes, mix tapes, outtake tapes, copy tapes, fly-in tapes, and back-up tapes. Write all labels with felt pen, not regular pen, and definitely not pencil.

ALIASES

Some bands like to keep a very low profile in the studio, sometimes going as far as using an alias on the work orders and tape labels. As these tapes are wheeled through lobbies and hallways where everyone can see, no one will know who the real band is. I once worked on a live record by the famous "Winston O'Boogie." (See index.) The tape label is broken down into three basic sections: project information, titles and locations, and the spine.

PROJECT INFORMATION

Filling in the project information section on the tape label is almost the same as filling in the tracksheet: it includes the date, studio used, artist, producer, engineer, assistant, and client. The label should also include:

- The location and level of alignment tones and record pad, track format, and any varispeed or noise reduction.

- Reference numbers on each reel for storage and record keeping. When the project is using only four or five multitrack reels, organization will be easy. Larger projects often have a variety of tapes and reels such as multitrack, ½", ¼", various digital and analog combinations. All tapes must be numbered and organized for quick and easy access. (See Chapter Twelve for more on tape control numbers.)

(AEH)   **(AEH)**

DATE: Aug. 2	REEL: M·1 OF: 5 ☒ 30 IPS ☐ 15 IPS ☐ DIG.
ARTIST: TUFF BEANS	REFERENCE: _____ nWm = 0VU
PRODUCER: D. BERG	
ENGINEER: HERBIE HYNDE	☒ 1K ☒ THIS REEL
ASSISTANT: A. REDDER	☒ 10K ☐ REEL# _____
CLIENT: BLACK INK PUB.	☒ 15K ☐ RECORD PAD
	☒ 50 Hz ☐ HEAD ☐ TAIL
	☒ 100 Hz ☐ N. R. _____

Left sidebar:

DATE: Aug. 2

TITLES:
TOO TUFF TO TAME
NIGHT OF THE LIVING BEANS
PARTY PARTY...
TONES

ARTIST: TUFF BEANS

SPEED: 30 IPS

REEL M 1 OF 5

TONES ON:
☒ THIS REEL
☐ REEL# _____

LIBRARY: 637.1.1.

☒ MASTER ☐ COPY
☐ SAFETY ☐ CLONE

☐ 48TK ☐ 32TK ☒ 24TK ☐ 16TK ☐ 8TK ☐ 2TK

TITLES	TAKE	LOCATE / CTL	TIME	COMMENTS
TOO TUFF TO TAME	4	:20	4:00	HTL
NIGHT OF THE LIVING BEANS	1	5:30	3:10	TL
PARTY PARTY PARTY PARTY PARTY		10:40	3:00	TL
ALIGNMENT TONES			5:00	HTL
1K. 10K. 15K. 100hz. 50hz				
RECORD PAD			1:00	TL
TUNING TONES			:30	

FS - FALSE START	C - COMPLETE	HL - HEAD LEADER	TL - TAIL LEADER	HTL - HEAD AND TAIL LEADER
INC - INCOMPLETE	H - HOLD	HM - HEAD MARK	TM - TAIL MARK	HTM - HEAD AND TAIL MARK

Figure 8.3. Tape Label

- A section showing whether the complete tape is a master, slave, safety master, or equalized copy of a master. However, sometimes one reel holds both masters and slaves. (See Chapter Nine for more on safeties and slaves.)

If the tape label (fig. 8.3.) is on a master reel, each song probably originated from various work reels. It is generally assumed that all analog tapes within a project are at least the same brand, the same batch and that they all use the same alignment.

TITLES AND LOCATIONS

The title section of the tape label may seem like it holds the same information as the title section of the takesheet. However, takesheets are used to organize work reels *before* a song is edited and assembled. This title information isn't normally written on the tape label, as the information will soon change. Tapes are labeled *after* all editing and assembly is complete, and the final take is established. A single reel can have many takesheets, all describing the complete contents of the reel. The label is a summary of these takesheets. According to fig. 8.3.:

- "Too Tuff To Tame" starts at 0:20, and is about 4 minutes long. Take 4 is being used as the master and is marked HTL, head and tail leadered.

- Then "Night of the Living Beans" starts at 5:30, and is about 3 minutes long. Take 1 is the master and is marked "TL," tail leadered. The tail leader of the previous song on the reel is this song's head leader.

- The last song on the reel "Party, Party, Party, Party, Party" starts at 10:40, and the take is not noted. This may mean that it is edited together from different takes. It is 3 minutes long, and also marked TL,

- After the songs are the alignment tones. According to the label, the total tones are 2 minutes 30 seconds long. Each tone lasts 30 seconds. The tones are also head and tail leadered. After the tones is a record pad used for the record alignment.

- Last is a tuning tone, usually A-440. The tuner will be aligned daily using this tone for the band to tune their instruments.

SPINE

Whatever format your tapes are, the information on the spine includes the date, artist, titles, slave and master information for each song and reel number. When locating reels in the tape vault, where tapes are stored like shelves of books, there must be enough information on the spines to differentiate one tape from another.

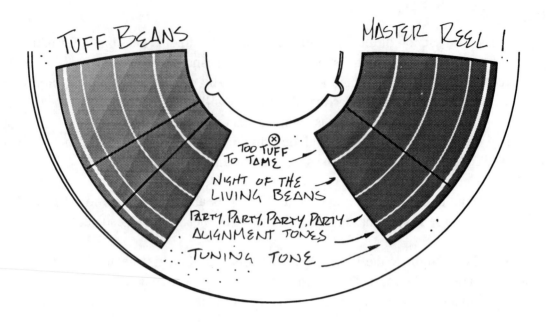

Figure 8.4. Labeling The Reel

LABELING THE REEL

Labeling the reel makes things far easier when locating songs. Figure 8.4. All reels look the same once they are out of the box, so each reel should be labeled with the project and reel number. Writing the individual songs on the reel is easier than having to rely on the machine's counter number every time a location is needed. Labeling the reel is especially useful when no leaders have been installed.

PROGRESS CHART

During record projects, some producers and engineers find it helpful to keep a progress chart hanging on the wall of the control room. Figure 8.5. This chart shows each song, and all the instruments to be recorded. When each track on a song is finished, the section is marked with an X. Anyone can look at this chart and see exactly what has been recorded and what is needed to complete the project.

	DRUMS	BASS	GTR1	GTR2	GTR3	KBDS	VOX	BKGD	PERC	MIX
PARTY PARTY PARTY	X	X	X	X		X		X	X	
TOO TUFF TO TAME	X	X	X	X	X	X				
WIENER WATER SOUP	X	X	X	X						
FT. McMURRAY STOMP	X	X	X	X	X					
NIGHT OF THE LIVING BEANS	X					X	X	X		
I CAN'T REALLY SING.	X	X	X	X		X				
YOU PUNCHED MY HEART RIGHT IN THE FACE.	X	X	X			X				
KRAFT DINNER	X	X	X							

Figure 8.5. Progress Chart

. . . .

Summary

Chapter Eight explained about what is expected of the assistant engineer during the recording of basic tracks:

- Making any changes, including microphones and their parameters, cables, and patches and headphones before the tapes start rolling.

- Keeping track of cues as the basic tracks are recorded.

- Running all the machines as the "tape operator."

- Keeping track of all paperwork, including takesheets, tape labels, labeling the reels, and updating the progress chart.

CHAPTER NINE

. . . .

After Basic Tracks

When the producer feels there is enough music recorded for a master take of a song, he will often have the musicians come in from the studio and listen to each take to express their opinion, approval, or disapproval. Although this determination is usually the producer's domain, most producers will respect a musician's input. If the musicians are hired guns they will usually just play the part until the producer is satisfied, with minimal input regarding choices of takes.

The producer will tell you which take he wants to hear first. Take all tracks on the multitrack machine out of *record-ready*, then cue up the correct take. They do not want to hear take 1 when they ask to hear take 2. Neither do they want to hear false starts. Wait until everyone is in the room before pressing *play*.

When all the musicians are in the control room listening, give one of them the engineer's chair. As they listen back to all the takes, you may want to sneak out to the studio and clean up coffee cups, ashtrays, cables, and anything else out of place. If the engineer wants to hear another take, or a section of another take while you're in the studio, he should be able to look at the counter locate numbers on the takesheet and transport the tape himself. As you clean up, listen to the music through the headphones strewn throughout the studio. When the song is almost over, return to the control room, in case anyone needs anything.

After all the takes have been heard, note if anyone states a preference. Later in the session, after doing many more takes, someone will undoubtedly wonder which was the early favorite. When everyone agrees that the performances recorded are enough to work with, the producer may want to do any number of things. The following tend to be among the most common:

EDITS

Most songs you hear today are a combination of many different takes. A song is often recorded many times, using the same tempo and structure. The engineer might then edit together a choice version of the song containing all the best parts from all the passes. For example, he may use the first chorus from take 2, the second chorus from take 4, and the verses from take 3, and combine them all to create one final choice take. The band may also play the song different ways, perhaps with different endings, then wait to hear the edited takes before deciding which version is best.

Whether the edits are analog or digital, they will either be insert edits, or assembly edits. Insert edits involve replacing unsatisfactory sections, for example replacing one chorus with a better chorus from another take. Assembly edits involve building the song from the beginning with the best sections of all the takes. Some songs are edited simply because they are too long.

Some producers never edit the song at the multitrack stage as they feel editing may take some of the magic away from the flow of the song. Jingles are rarely edited at the multitrack stage. Often they are written and recorded exactly 15, 30 or 60 seconds long for radio and TV spots, and editing them would change their exact timing. Editing takes time, and jingles are usually on a very tight schedule. Most jingle edits take place during mixdown, when shorter or longer versions of a spot are needed.

BEFORE THE EDITS

Often, before the engineer splices the multitrack tape, he rough mixes the song to an analog mixdown machine for trial edits. After confirming that the edits will work, he splices the multitrack tape. (The difference between a splice and an edit is, the tape is spliced, the music is edited.) Tape is traditionally spliced using razor blades and splicing tape, but as today's digital technology becomes more accessible, electronic editing is becoming increasingly common. Before any editing begins, you must be prepared to help with the following:

- Fresh sharp razor blades. Keep lots on hand, as the engineer may discard them after one or two splices. Demagnetize them so there is no chance of signal erasure where the razor contacts the tape. Open the cardboard sleeve holding the razor, but leave the razor within the sleeve. This way the engineer knows the razor is unused, yet easy for him to retrieve.

  When discarding used blades, don't just toss them into the trash. Either put them in a small used razor box or tape the razor's edge with adhesive tape before throwing it away, so whoever changes the trash bags won't accidentally get sliced. I accidentally cut my finger open during the recording of KISS's "Animalize" and got blood all over the multitrack machine. Gene praised me for "getting into the vibe."

- Sharpened white grease pencils. Rub the grease pencil, or china marker on a piece of scrap paper while spinning it on the paper, giving the pencil a good sharp point, then cut off the excess string. Subtle, yes — but it can be the attention to detail that makes clients and engineers want to work with you in the future.

- Leader tape. Ask the engineer if he wants paper or plastic leader, and what width and color of splicing tape he prefers.

- Outtake reels. Outtakes are the complete and incomplete takes, false starts and non-choice sections of a project. These sometimes take up many reels, and are not normally brought into the control room for the sessions. They stay in the vault.

- An edit reel. This reel holds the sections removed from the choice takes. Use a takesheet to mark all the edit pieces clearly, and to organize them by the song, section of the song, length of the section removed, the take, and the date. Leader edited sections by song, and write each song title on the leader tape. As well, write the titles on the reel. The edits must be totally organized in case the producer wants an edit put back into the song.

- Extra empty reels and boxes. Extra reels and boxes should always be available. Empty reels are needed to create the master reels. When you need an empty reel and don't have one, slice off the remains of an almost empty reel with a razor blade, or spool the tape off the reel directly into the trash can. Check first to make sure nothing important is being discarded.

- A clean splicing block. Before use, clean the splicing block with cotton and alcohol to remove any studio grime and grunge, then demagnetize the block. Some engineers prefer the kind of splicing block with the arms that flip down to hold the tape in the block. Some prefer the kind where the tape fits in snugly without any arms holding it in place. Most splicing blocks are made to fit two layers of tape. Both layers are cut, spliced together, and the excess sections of tape are removed.

- Clean hands. The oils on your fingers transfer onto tape, so clean hands are essential. Sometimes white cotton gloves are used on those rare occasions when digital tapes are physically spliced. However, razor blades and splicing tape are not normally used when editing in the digital domain. Digital editing involves synchronizing two digital machines, then transferring sections of a song from one machine to another, or internal editing using a computer hard drive.

DURING THE EDITS

When the engineer is editing, he is counting on you to help keep everything organized. You must:

- Stay at the desk. He may want you at the desk to solo specific tracks, such as the snare or kick drum track, to find the exact spot to mark.

- Keep up. As he is scrubbing the tape, (manually moving it back and forth over the heads to find the exact edit point) make sure he knows which head (*sync* or *repro*) he is monitoring and that he is at the right spot before the edit, and not, for example, on the wrong chorus.

- Use an additional machine. Many control rooms have access to more than one multitrack machine. If possible, use another machine for organizing the various sections of tape while the engineer edits on the main machine. If he needs a piece of tape from another reel, you can quickly find it using the second machine. This second machine can also be used throughout the session for organizing master reels, locating sections, editing, and leadering while the main machine is in use.

  Some engineers use different splicing angles for different sorts of edits. One angle might used if the edits are between songs, and another angle might be used if the edits are within a song. Other engineers find an angle on the splicing block that they like and use it for all edits. If you are helping with the splicing, use the angle he uses.

- Be quiet. Wait for the right moment to ask non-essential questions. Asking him what he thought of last night's *Canucks* game during an important edit may not be appropriate. Let him concentrate on what he is doing.

- Stay organized. In the daily log, keep track of the origin of every piece from a choice take. If any additional editing is needed, or if an edit needs to be put back in, the complete layout of where all the sections originated is available.

AFTER THE EDITS

When edits have shortened or lengthened a song's timing, the cue numbers will have changed. If possible, load the reel onto a second multitrack machine and, using headphones to avoid disturbing the rest of the session, write down the correct new numbers. Patch two tracks, such as vocals or ambiance tracks, out of the multitrack machine and into the input of a cassette tape machine. Put the cassette tape machine in *input*, and monitor the two tracks of the multitrack machine through the cassette tape machine's headphone output.

Undoing an Edit

Sometimes, edits need to be replaced, which means the splice must be opened, and the original section of the song returned. With clean hands, use your fingers to carefully to remove the piece of splicing tape. If this doesn't work, try careful use of a razor blade. If any glue from the splicing tape stays on the back of the audio tape, wrap up a ball of splicing tape with the sticky side out and pat the area to remove the excess glue. Find the right section of tape to be returned using the information in the daily log.

Practicing Your Edits

In off time, try practicing your edits. Maybe the engineer on your project will let you practice editing the outtakes. If not, use a house multitrack tape — after getting permission, of course. House tapes are used by the technical staff to test equipment and do alignments, and by assistants for learning purposes.

At one end of the reel, not in the middle, record a song or section of a song from a CD to two tracks of multitrack tape. Practice your editing skills by moving the verses around, or extending the ending — be creative. This is good practice for when you're called upon to do the leadering and assembly of master reels.

REPAIRS

Once a final master take is edited together, the producer may want to musically repair a section or sections of tracks. On many of today's rock albums, the producer will have the engineer record the whole band, but concentrate on getting the drums to sound right. After all the choice drum sections are edited together, certain spots on other tracks, such as the bass and guitars, may not flow over the splices smoothly. These spots, and perhaps other spots that aren't acceptable, will need to be repaired, or even completely re-recorded.

For example, the drums are edited together from many different takes. While they may sound great, some of the edits can be heard on the bass guitar track. These minor sections are often repaired right after the edits, and before moving on to another song. If the whole bass track is unsatisfactory, it might be completely re-recorded, often after all the basic tracks are complete.

Before starting the repairs, take all tracks on the multitrack machine out of *record-ready* except the track(s) to be worked on. If recording a totally new track, check the tracksheet to make sure the intended track is empty. If additional tracks are recorded, these cease becoming repairs, and become overdubs. (See Chapter Ten for more on recording overdubs.)

MUSICIAN IN THE STUDIO

When a musician must repair a track, the rest of the musicians will often leave the studio. As they do, go out into the studio and unplug all their headphones. Signal blaring through all the headphones will be picked up by the active microphones. Don't change the volume on the headphone boxes, as they are set to where each musician wants them. If there is any unwanted noise, like buzzing amplifiers or rattling snares, check with the engineer before doing anything about it.

MUSICIAN IN THE CONTROL ROOM

When recording an electric instrument, such as an amplified guitar, the musician may prefer to leave the studio and play in the control room. As the sound doesn't emanate acoustically from the instrument, the engineer would only hear the output of amplifier through the microphones. Though the musician moves from the studio to the control room, the sound must stay the same for continuity when punching in and out of the existing track, so the amplifiers stay where they are. You may have to extend the cables on the instrument for the musician to move from the studio to the control room.

The musician playing in the control room may not want to use headphones, since the music will be pumping through the main speakers during the repair. The only disadvantage here is for the engineer. He usually needs to hear everything from his own perspective, often soloing tracks to listen for various things. If the musician is using the main speakers for his cue, the engineer must monitor the song to the musician's wants and needs. For instance, if the musician wants more bass, the engineer must turn up the bass.

The musician must be positioned where he can hear the speakers in a comfortable spot. If he is all the way over on one side of the room, he may not feel the impact of the song as he would if he were in the middle of the stereo spectrum. Some studios have extra speakers for musicians to use while playing in the control room.

INSTRUMENT SETUP SHEETS

As the edits and repairs are taking place, and before another song is started, you must document the setup of the instruments and amplifiers. Use the setup sheet to write down the instrument, its placement in the studio and its settings, the microphones and their parameters, the inputs on the desk, the signal processing, the bussing, the patching, and the track(s) recorded on. Once the sound is documented, the exact same sound can be returned at any time in the future. There are many reasons a sound is documented, including:

- After spending most of a session getting a good sound, time runs out before the part is recorded correctly. The producer wants to start the next session with the same sound, and continue recording.

- The producer may very happy with a sound recorded on another song in the project, and wants to use the same sound for another song.

- If a part in the song is changed later in the project, or section of a track is accidentally erased, the sound can be returned, and the track can be repaired.

CREATING AND DOCUMENTING

To log the settings on equipment quickly and accurately, you must use a setup sheet. Figure 9.1. Because there is no standard method of writing down a setup, one specific sheet cannot cover all the different options: fig. 9.1. is an example. Many equipment manuals include master sheets of equipment faceplates. Photocopy the pages, showing the faceplates, and leaving enough space on the sheet for logging the internal settings. Most studios already have these copies.

If there are no master sheets, draw them yourself, making sure they are accurate. However, sometimes reproductions of the faceplates are not needed. If the settings on a certain unit can be written using numbers, use a plain sheet of paper to write the setup. Again, your studio procedure dictates.

Document everything clearly and precisely. Sometimes a Polaroid camera is used to capture exact placement, or a cassette recorder is used to dictate the exact equipment settings. Your setup sheet should include:

- Date. Clearly write the date of each recording for cross referencing. Anyone should be able to look at the tracksheet, refer to the corresponding date in the log, find the setup sheet, and find any information regarding the sound.

- Track information. The band or artist's name, the song title, the individual track numbers, and location of the sound within the song must appear. Some tracks have more than one instrument at different sections, such as track 15, which contains basic guitar in the choruses, and a tambourine in the verses. See the tracksheet (fig. 6.2.).

- Instrument. Write the name and model of the instrument used, including its settings, any specific tunings, knob settings, switches, and, if possible, the apparent age and gauge of any strings used. If necessary, note the musician's name as well.

- Effects. Effects boxes, their settings, whether on or off during the performance, the order in which they appear, battery or AC powered, and anything else that might affect the audio signal must be logged.

- Amplification. Include the placement and identity of the amplifier, the settings of the knobs, the specific input used, and any important internal amplifier information, such as installation of special tubes or cards. Show the setup sheet to the musician to see if there is anything you may have overlooked.

- Microphones and placement. Write down the microphone's make, model, serial number, exact placement, respective pads and polar patterns. If you are returning to the same sound next session, but can't leave the equipment set up, use white adhesive tape on the floor to show precise placement of the microphones and amplifiers. Label the adhesive tape with the date, song title, and part. If you aren't planning to return to the sound in the very near future, remember that adhesive tape on the floor won't last very long.

- Desk and inputs. The inputs to the desk, the line/microphone level, any equalization and limiting, individual channel fader levels, bussing, and patching need to be logged. Most engineers want to use the same channels for repairs as used for the original recording. If you are fortunate enough to work in a studio that has a computer to store and recall these settings, store all desk settings, then double check the data disk. Label the data disk, make a safety copy of the disk as backup, and store it appropriately.

- Outboard. Write down any outboard equipment settings, both internal and external, front and rear, including the inputs and outputs used. If the studio owns more than one unit of the same model, note the one used. If using rental equipment, write down the make and serial number of the unit, and the rental company. The engineer will definitely want the same unit when re-doing the setup. When any processing, such as an equalizer, is in the path but not active, include it in the setup sheet, stating its status. Although inactive, it may change the sound slightly.

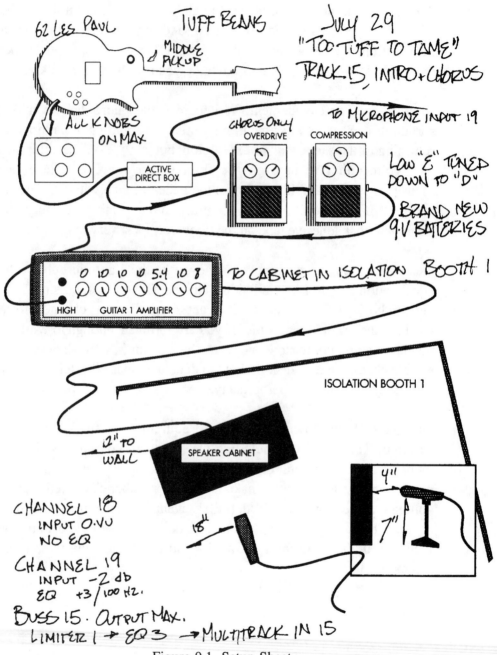

Figure 9.1. Setup Sheet

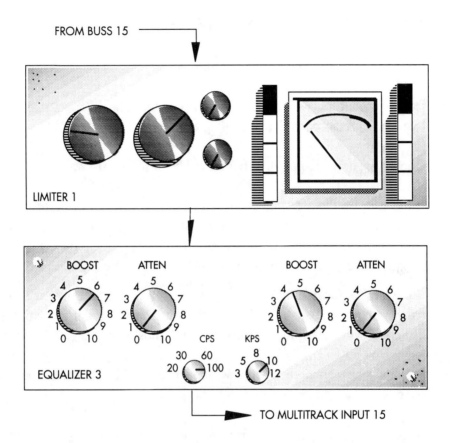

Keep the setup sheet clear and organized, as you may not be the person re-creating the setup. Once the setup is completely logged, go over the path from signal to tape again to double check that the setup sheet is correct.

If time permits, write down every sound recorded, no matter how minor it may seem to you. If it isn't important, it wouldn't be on tape. For example, the producer leaves the session early, and a musician records a rough idea to tape, just using a quick setup, and then moves on. Weeks later, the producer hears the part, loves it, and wants the musician to re-do it correctly, using the same sound.

RECORDING BASIC TRACKS FOR ANOTHER SONG

As everyone returns to the studio for the next song's basic tracks, you need to:

- Load the multitrack machine with a virgin tape. The engineer may want to record over earlier unacceptable unedited takes.

- Cue up the correct spot, then put all tracks into *record-ready.*

- If the strip for the old song is written on adhesive tape, write the song title on the end of the adhesive tape. Remove the strip of tape from the desk and place it on the control room window for storage. Replace the strip on the desk with a new length of adhesive tape for the new song.

  If the track information is not written on adhesive tape, but written on the actual strip on the desk, use the tracksheet to re-write the track information on the strip. Either way, the basic track information will most likely remain the same.

- Prepare a new tracksheet, a few takesheets, and a few tape labels for the new song.

- If a click generator is used, you may be required to change the tempo, after the old click tempo is written down. Confirm this with the engineer.

- As the rest of the musicians return to the studio to continue recording, go out with them and plug in all the headphones. Musicians love to put on headphones first, and plug them in second. This usually blasts their ears out, but they never learn.

- Help the musicians with any of their session needs. When everyone in the studio is ready, return to the control room and prepare for the next basic track.

ASSEMBLING MASTER REELS

Whether recording basics or mixing, the choice takes tend to be scattered throughout many reels. These choice takes need to be removed from their original reels, and placed on master reels. Master reels are reels that contain only the choice takes. The average album project (as it has been traditionally called) might fill five or six analog multitrack reels. The number of mix reels can vary from few to many.

You may assemble the master reels either as the choice takes are established, or when all the basic tracks are finished. Either way, all takes need to be timed so they will fit comfortably on a reel. Don't overload a master reel. Each master reel box also needs correct labels with new location numbers. Of course, if the mixes are stored digitally, some of the following might not be applicable. To assemble master reels:

1) Find the reel with the first master take, and load it on the multitrack machine. Transport the tape to the beginning of the song.

2) Splice the tape at least 15 seconds before the count of the song. If a slave of the song is needed in the future, there must be ample space before the song starts for the timecodes to synchronize. (See Chapter Ten for more on timecodes and synchronization.)

3) Remove the original reel from the take-up side of the machine, and replace it with the now empty master reel 1. Load it with a few feet of blank multitrack tape. Splice in a length of leader tape, and splice the beginning of the first song to the end of the leader.

4) Use a felt pen to write the title of the song on the leader, so when the tape is parked at the beginning of a song, anyone can see which song is loaded.

5) Forward the reel to the end of the first master take, and splice in a leader, again leaving ample tape before splicing. Future overdubs may extend beyond the present ending.

6) Remove the master reel from the take-up side of the machine, and load the original reel. Splice the ends together, and forward the reel off. This reel is now less one song.

7) Write "Pulled to Master," or simply PTM and the date on the box that originally held the master take. On the master reel box, state which reel the take came from, and the take number, if possible. Some choice takes might be edited combinations of many different takes.

8) Do the assembly so the splices can't be physically heard. Turn down the monitors, and listen to the tape crossing the heads. If you can hear a splice go by, stop tape, open the splice and re-do it. These splices may pass over the heads hundreds of times, so they need to be very secure.

9) Find the reel that has the next song to be put on the master reel, and load it on the machine. Repeat.

10) Continue until master reel 1 is full, then start over on master reel 2. Each reel is labeled, for example reel 2 of 5. The tones either have their own reel, or are placed at the end of the first reel. When all basic tracks are complete, and all master reels are assembled, the session can focus on overdubs.

.   .   .   .

Summary

Chapter Nine explained about what is expected of the assistant engineer after the basic tracks are recorded:

- Helping the engineer create a master take with organization before, during and after the multitrack edits.

- Repairs of tracks recorded during the basics.

- Creating setup sheets, and documenting all sounds recorded.

- Assembling all the choice basic tracks on master reels.

CHAPTER TEN

. . . .

Recording Overdubs

The basic tracks are now recorded. The songs have all been edited using the best pieces to create the choice versions. The individual tracks that are being kept from the basic sessions have all been repaired, and everything that needs documenting has been written down. All songs have been assembled onto master tapes.

It is time to move from basics to overdubs. Overdubs are additional recordings added to a song after the basic tracks are complete, often one instrument at a time. This is usually where the most hours are logged in a large project. Overdubs can take weeks, months or even years on very large projects.

As the engineer tells you exactly what changes to make, write everything down on your pad of paper so you don't have to ask him a second time. For example, if the engineer wants to record a vocal overdub on another song, using a Neumann U-87 in channel 25 on the desk, with a limiter then an equalizer on the channel, and he wants to record it on track 13, you had better write that down.

Whenever moving to a new song and changing a setup, you can do it one of two ways. Either change tapes and load the new song first, then set up the studio. This way the engineer can prepare the desk with a new monitor mix, and the musician can hear the song while you set up the studio. Or you can set up the studio, then change the tapes, so the musician can set up while the tapes are being changed. The argument over which way is best has created quite a few brawls down at the "Real to Reel Bar and Grille."

Note that much of this chapter applies to reels of tape. With many studios today using multitrack digital cassettes and hard drive storage systems, some of the following might not be applicable.

FINDING THE SONG

CHANGING REELS

When you are changing reels to find another song, follow this procedure:

1) Disarm any tracks in *record-ready*.

2) To avoid hearing the recorded program zipping past the heads, switch the machine to *input,* as this keeps the microphones active. If the musicians stay in the studio during the changeover, the people in the control room will want to talk with the people in the studio while you change tapes. You could also mute the output of the desk, but this also mutes communication to and from the studio.

3) Wind the tape to the end of the reel. Put the collar around it, or use a small piece of adhesive tape to hold the end of the tape in place.

4) Get the old tracksheet from the desk after checking with the engineer that all updates have been noted. You may not know if a track was modified or erased while you were doing something else. Again, tracksheets not in use are always kept in the box with the tape.

5) If the VSO was used, deactivate it, and write the new speed on the tracksheet on the applicable tracks recorded. (See later in this chapter for more on VSO.)

6) Remove the reel from the machine, place it in the correct box and put it with the rest of the tapes.

7) Gather all the paperwork for the particular song. If the collection of lyrics, setup sheets and notes becomes too large to keep with the daily log, store it in a large clearly labeled manila envelope.

8) Find the reel containing the new song to be worked on, load it on the spindle, and thread it up correctly. Then put up the head protector.

9) Open the new tracksheet and put it on the desk facing the engineer.

10) You may need to change or re-label the strip with the new song information. (See later in this chapter for more on setting up the desk for overdubs.)

FINDING A SONG WITHIN A REEL

Now the correct reel is loaded on the machine. If all songs on the reel are properly leadered and labeled, finding the beginning of each song should be easy. But not all reels are leadered and labeled. To find a song on an unleadered, unlabeled reel:

• Rewind to the beginning of the reel, zero the tape counter, then fast-forward to the correct spot using the numbers written on the tape label.

• If counter numbers are not available, or you don't wish to rewind all the way to the beginning of the reel, go to approximately where you think the song begins. If you are alone in the room, play the song through the monitors. If anyone, except the engineer is in the room, find the spot in silence using headphones.

Shuttle the machine back and forth until you find the beginning of the correct song, then zero the tape counter. Some people press the tape against the head as the machine is in rewind, listening as the quiet spots zip by. This is not recommended, as it is akin to taking an electric sander to the head of the machine. It also gets the heads very dirty very fast.

• Often, remote controls allow total control of the counter numbers. These numbers and can easily be changed and re-set. To avoid going all the way to the beginning of the song to zero the tape counter, simply find the very end of the song. If the reel is tails out, the end of a song should be faster to find. Once there, look at the tape label and find the length of the song. Enter this number on the remote, then rewind to zero, which should be the beginning of the song.

- If the tape has been recorded with timecode, patch from the timecode track into the input of the code reader. Get the exact numbers and go directly to the desired spot — providing the timecode reader is receiving correct information, and the cues and song locations are correctly written down. (See later in this chapter for more on timecodes.) With digital tapes the CTL/A-time numbers are established when the tape is formatted.

- Once you have found the song, and the tape is parked at the correct spot, set any specific parameters listed on the tracksheet. If any speed changes are noted on the tracksheet, set the VSO to the correct speed, leave it off, and ask the engineer when he wants it activated.

- If noise reduction is noted, set it up on the appropriate tracks, activate it and tell the engineer.

- Check that the intended track, in this case track 13, is open on the tracksheet. If there is something on the track, the engineer either doesn't realize, or wants to record additional instruments on the open areas. For example, notice that on track 15 the guitar occurs only in the intro and choruses. This leaves open space in the verses, so a tambourine was recorded during the verses. As the two instruments never play at the same time, they can occupy the same track.

VSO

The Variable Speed Oscillator (also called the varispeed or VSO) allows the user to change the speed of the multitrack machine in fine increments. Occasionally, after the basics are complete, the client wants the tempo of a song slightly changed. Any changes to the speed of the machine also changes the tempo and tuning of the recorded music. As the pitch of the musical instruments on tape is changed, so is the pitch of the tuning tone on the alignment reel. This tone can therefore be used to re-calibrate the tuner to the new tuning of the song.

The varispeed is always off during basic tracks. If the tempo of a song is not working, the click is changed and the song is recorded at a tempo that works. It is after the basic track has been recorded that VSOs are used. It would be a massive inconvenience and expense to go back, set up all the instruments and microphones just to re-record one song with a slight tempo change.

SETTING UP THE STUDIO

Now that the proper tape is cued up and the parameters on the machine are set, the engineer can ready the desk for the overdub while you organize the studio. Often the turnover from basics to overdubs occurs mid-session. Before a new setup is started, the old one is usually broken down, but in some cases, the setup is left intact. For example, if the engineer wants to use part of the setup again, or if the setup needs to be documented and there isn't time to do it between the changeover of songs.

The most common setup for a vocal or single instrument overdub is one microphone in the studio. This is not necessarily the only way, or even the right way. You will discover that there is no right or wrong way to record. According to your pad of paper, follow these steps:

1) Mute channel 13 on the desk.

2) Go into the studio and lay out a small carpet. This eliminates the possibilities of floor squeaks and toe taps being picked up by the microphone. Place the carpet where the musician can be easily seen from the control room.

3) Perhaps set up baffles behind the musician to reduce unwanted room ambiance.

4) Bring out the microphone and stand, and set them up. To save time, use any stands and cables already set up. Set up the microphone, cables and headphones as described in Chapter Three.

5) Put a jug of water, or cup of tea with honey on a small table nearby. Keep them filled throughout the session. These are not for refreshment, but to help ease the throat. During vocals, don't fill the water glass with ice cold water, as cold water can strain the vocal chords.

6) When a music stand is needed, put the appropriate lyrics or sheet music, a sharpened pencil, and maybe a light on the stand. Perhaps drape a small towel over the stand to absorb and block sound from reflecting back into the microphone.

7) The musician may want a chair or stool to sit on.

8) On some recordings, a certain mood may be needed. Sometimes the musician wants the lights down low to evoke a more creative atmosphere. Candles or incense are sometimes used to create a mood, although this is not always the case. During jingle situations, with professional musicians and tight schedules, there will normally be no candles or incense — unless, of course, the clients are Moonies.

SETTING UP THE DESK

Now that you have set up the microphones and headphones for the overdub, return to the control room to help prepare the desk and patchbay. The engineer may prefer to set up the desk himself, or he may let you do it. If any patches are needed, make the patches, then perhaps do a headphone cue mix for the musician.

DESK STATUS

Depending on the engineer's preference, the desk status may or may not stay the same for overdubs as it was for basics. If the main faders need to be changed from microphone inputs to multitrack returns, channels need to be re-zeroed so the equalization and processing used for the microphone inputs is not applied to the multitrack returns. For example, during basic tracks, when the desk was in microphone mode, the engineer set the equalization on channel 10, the hi-hat, Now that the desk is in line mode, channel 10 has a cymbal track returning on it. This equalization, if left activated, is applied to the cymbal. This is not what the engineer wants.

SIGNAL ROUTING

With the desk in the correct status, route the incoming microphone signals to the multitrack machine either through busses on the desk, or through direct inputs at the patchbay.

Channel routing follows no rules. Often many channels on the desk are routed to one track on the multitrack, and often one channel is routed to many tracks. During basics, if the situation called for it, the engineer could buss all the microphones on the all instruments to one track, then buss one microphone from one guitar to the other twenty-three tracks for one long loud twenty-three-track guitar solo.

To route the signal according to the tracksheet, follow these steps:

1) Return to the control room and prepare channel 25 on the desk, the input for the microphone. According to your pad of paper, track 13 is the intended track for the overdub.

2) Check that channel 25 on the desk is not a channel the engineer wants to leave set up for future use.

3) Set the microphone/line switch on channel 25 to *microphone*. Remove any equalization, patches, or subgroups on the channel. Lower all sends and, if necessary, activate the phantom power.

4) Put track 13 in *record-ready,* which should switch it to *input*. The instrument to be recorded must be monitored for correct sound and input level. On the desk, press buss 13 on channel 25. This is *not* the only way to send the signal to the multitrack, but it is a common way. The engineer will tell you if he prefers a different method.

5) Patch in the limiting and equalization, deactivate the equalization from the signal, and set the limiter to a moderate level. The engineer will set them when necessary.

Depending on the engineer's preference, the limiting and equalization processing could be patched either before or after the buss. If this processing is patched *before* the buss output (out of the insert send, into the processing then back again into the insert return of the channel) the processed signal goes to all busses pressed on that channel.

If the signal is patched *after* the buss (from the buss output into the limiting and equalization processing then back into the multitrack input), every time the engineer wants to change tracks you must change the track input patch.

TESTING THE INPUTS

Once the desk is set, check the input from the microphone for proper connection. Follow these steps:

1) Un-mute channel 13, the return from track 13 on the multitrack machine. Turn up the level and, to hear if the microphone input 25 is working, bring up the fader level of channel 25. When you hear the room noise in the studio being routed from the microphone through channel 25 to track 13, bring the fader level on channel 13 back down.

2) On channel 13, set the cue send switch to *pre-fader* and turn up the cue send level. Put the master cue send level just over half way.

3) Go into the studio, put on the headphones, and speak into the microphone. You should hear yourself in the headphones. The control room will not hear you because their monitor for channel 25 is off.

4) If the signal level needs adjustment, go into the control room and adjust it.

5) Once the level is set, add any reverbs or delays in the headphone mix. Go back out to the studio and check the headphones again. As you speak, listen to the reverb level. Is it loud enough? Is it in stereo? Can you hear everything? Set everything up so the musician can walk out, put on the headphones and begin.

REST OF THE DESK

Before changing the desk completely, check again that the engineer does not want to keep any of the existing channels set up. Though everything is documented, he may want to keep an instrument set up for later use. To change the desk over from basics to overdubs:

- When time is a major factor, don't zero the equalization on each channel, simply deactivate it.

- Pull all the faders down, and remove any subgroups.

- Turn all the sends down. Leave the master send and return levels alone, as they are still being used.

- Pull all the applicable patches, leaving the ones still in use, such as effects sends and returns.

- If the monitor source is being changed from the monitor section of the desk to the main faders, change any applicable patches. For example, if multitrack return 8 on the monitor section has a limiter patched into it, remove the limiter from the monitor section and place it into main fader 8, which is now the main monitor.

- The cue system may get its own echo plate. If so, patch this off an unused send so a musician can hear his echo in the headphones.

- When the session changes from one song to another, the strip on the desk needs to be re-labeled with the new track layout. As basics are over, each song recorded should have its own adhesive strip somewhere in the control room.

SETTING UP A PREVIOUS SOUND

When the time comes to return to a sound that was documented earlier in the project, setup should be relatively easy if the original was correctly logged. If the equipment is still set up, especially if the microphones and amplifiers haven't been moved, the job of returning to the original sound is much easier. If the total setup has been broken down, you need to start from scratch. To return to a previous sound:

1) Look on the tracksheet for the original recording date, go to that date in the daily log, and find the correct setup. Of course, if no date is written on the individual track, you know it was recorded during the basic.

2) Set up the instrument and microphones as detailed on the setup sheet (fig. 9.1.). If possible, use the same pieces of outboard, channels and microphones that were used during the original recording. If the setup was correctly written down, you should not have a problem returning to the sound.

3) After completing the setup, for the most accurate result, load the multitrack machine with the song containing the sound you are re-creating. Have the musician play along with the original, and A/B them. (Switch back and forth between the original sound on tape and the live sound being played.) The goal is to recreate the original sound. If there is a difference between the two sounds, trace the signal flow and make sure it is how the original was logged.

Realize that no matter how diligently the original was logged, the same sound simply might not return. The engineer will realize this, and he will work with the new sound until it matches the old. He may simply use the sound set up as a starting point for a new sound.

Often, if a project is in lock-out, certain setups that the engineer likes will just stay set up. If there are enough channels on the desk, some channels might stay set up for the duration of the project, such as a vocal setup. Then, whenever the singer gets the urge to record a track, he simply walks out and sings without having to wait around while you set everything up.

MONITOR MIX

A monitor mix is a rough setting of all the levels, panning, and effects of inputs returning to the desk, either live or from a multitrack machine, to let everyone in the control room hear what is being, and what has been, recorded.

If the engineer doesn't begin setting up a monitor mix, sit in the main chair and start. Bring up the levels of the instruments, applying the sends and panning them way the engineer does it. Generally, set everything up except the limiting and equalization processing. That's the engineer's territory.

If the engineer always uses certain setups, such as the hi-hat all the way to the right, match his setup. Some engineers like to set the record levels so the multitrack returns come back to the desk at zero, where all faders are at the same level. (Note that zero is not all the way off, but at optimum fader level.) The engineer's way is the right way. Remember, it is *his* session, and you are his assistant.

This is a good time for you to use your ears. Do some reasonable panning and sends to reverbs. This is not the time to experiment with wild effects. Just do a basic mix. If the engineer hears you can do good, quick, monitor mixes, he might in time let you spend more time behind the desk, which is the ultimate goal.

CUE MIX

The cue mix, like the tape monitor in the control room, is sent off the channel returns from the multitrack machine. When you are doing the cue mixes, put on the engineer's headphones and match the panning and levels to the engineer's monitor mix. For example, if the engineer has the rhythm guitar track all the way to the left, match it in the headphone mix. Keep the master headphone mix at a reasonable level, not so loud that it blasts the musician when he puts on the headphones. Better he ask for it louder than quieter.

The importance of a good cue mix cannot be overstated. A musician recording with good headphone mix can be the difference between an average performance, and an outstanding one.

RECORDING

Now everything is ready. The engineer has the right monitor mix, he is at the beginning of the song, the multitrack machine is in *record-ready* on track 13. The microphones, limiting and equalization, and headphones are set and working normally, and he has the song cue numbers in front of him.

As the tape starts rolling, and the red record lights are on, write the new track on the tracksheet, and document the setup. Watch that all the equipment is reacting properly and everything is going smoothly. Try not to leave the control room while any machine is in *record.*

PUNCHING IN AND OUT

If you are the tape operator (simply called the tape-op) you will be the person running the tape machines, and punching in and out of *record* at exact spots during a song. If the producer tells you "punch in on the down beat of the third bar in the second chorus, and punch out at the end of the chorus," you must use the cues written down, your ears, your musical abilities and your experience to punch in and out correctly. Remember these points:

• Do not press *record* if you are at all unsure of where the in and out points are. If you don't know, say that you want to hear the section once first to hear the correct spots. Punching in or out at the wrong spot may be disastrous, creating hours of extra work for everyone. It may also limit your chances of any engineering on the rest of the project.

• Perhaps create a safety track by bouncing the section over to another track. Then if any important part on the master track is accidentally erased, a safety of the original is still intact. Digital safety tracks are routinely made, then bounced back into the master. An analog safety track is of course a generation down, therefore not quite the same quality, but still usable.

- Make sure both you and the musician know where the engineer wants the punch-ins and punch-outs.

- When repeatedly punching in the same part, go back to the same spot every time, about eight to ten seconds ahead of the punch-in point. This helps you count the correct amount of bars before punching in, and it also helps the musician get to know where he is within the song. On some multitrack machines, the exact in and out punches can be programmed into the multitrack machine's internal memory. The machine then automatically punches in and out at the correct places.

- Don't punch in or out on a sustaining note.

- Know the response time of the multitrack machine. Are the punch-ins and punch-outs fast or slow? Check the crossfade times on digital machines, and adjust as necessary.

- After the take, go back and listen to the punch points. Sometimes a gulp sound is heard at the in or out point. If you accidentally record over something important, *you* will be making the gulp sound!

- Punches are meant to be clean and not heard. Sometimes the relays on analog machines are heard just when the record button is pressed, but this hiccup is not recorded.

CHANGING TRACKS

Often, especially with vocals, more than one track is recorded. The singer might sing a song three or four times, just to get the feel of a song. As each vocal pass is recorded on a different track, each track returns to a different channel on the desk. You must change each track on the machine and its corresponding channel return.

For example, as the tape is rewinding to the beginning of the song for the second pass, the engineer will take the previous track, 13, out of *record* and put the next one, 14, in *record-ready*. This means he wants to record another pass on track 14. Follow these steps:

1) Check that track 14 is open.

2) As the cue level and effects for the singer are sent to the headphones off of channel 13 on the desk, match these levels to the return of channel 14.

3) Move the patch cord from the input of track 13, over to the input of track 14. The singer shouldn't hear any change in the headphones, or even be aware of any technicalities in the control room. Let him sing with no distractions. Depending on how the engineer has the microphone input channel set up, this step may not be needed.

4) Make sure track 13 is out of *record-ready* on the multitrack machine.

5) Mute track 13 from the room monitor and the headphones, including all effects.

6) Number each vocal pass on the tracksheet, and label each one as a work track.

7) Another option is to patch the return of multitrack 14 into the input of channel 13 on the desk. With track 14 returning to channel 13, all the cue levels and sends stay the same. This works great until the musician wants to hear both tracks, 13 and 14 at the same time.

8) As the vocals are being recorded, write down the tape machine counter numbers on the lyric sheet on each line of the song. These line numbers are more detailed than the cue numbers written on the tracksheet, so any line in the song can be instantly found for a punch-in.

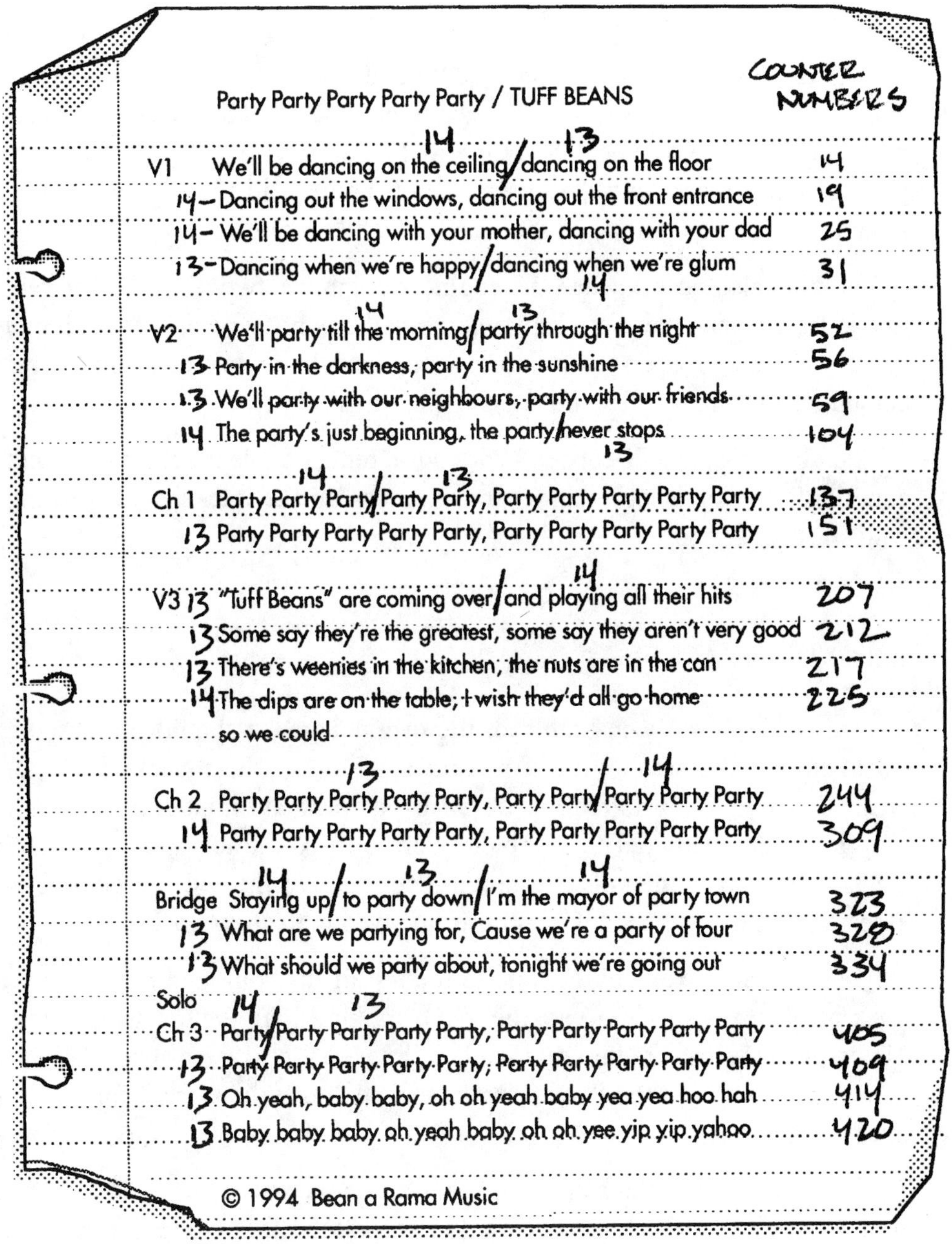

Party Party Party Party Party / TUFF BEANS

COUNTER NUMBERS

V1 We'll be dancing on the ceiling / dancing on the floor — 14 / 13 — 14

Dancing out the windows, dancing out the front entrance — 14 — 19

We'll be dancing with your mother, dancing with your dad — 14 — 25

Dancing when we're happy / dancing when we're glum — 13 — 31

V2 We'll party till the morning / party through the night — 14 / 13 — 52

Party in the darkness, party in the sunshine — 13 — 56

We'll party with our neighbours, party with our friends — 13 — 59

The party's just beginning, the party never stops — 14 — 104

Ch 1 Party Party Party / Party Party, Party Party Party Party Party — 14 / 13 — 137

Party Party Party Party Party, Party Party Party Party Party — 13 — 151

V3 "Tuff Beans" are coming over / and playing all their hits — 13 / 14 — 207

Some say they're the greatest, some say they aren't very good — 13 — 212

There's weenies in the kitchen, the nuts are in the can — 13 — 217

The dips are on the table; I wish they'd all go home so we could — 14 — 225

Ch 2 Party Party Party Party Party, Party Party / Party Party Party — 13 / 14 — 244

Party Party Party Party Party, Party Party Party Party Party — 14 — 309

Bridge Staying up / to party down / I'm the mayor of party town — 14 / 13 / 14 — 323

What are we partying for, Cause we're a party of four — 13 — 328

What should we party about, tonight we're going out — 13 — 334

Solo

Ch 3 Party / Party Party Party Party, Party Party Party Party Party — 14 / 13 — 405

Party Party Party Party Party, Party Party Party Party Party — 13 — 409

Oh yeah, baby baby, oh oh yeah baby yea yea hoo hah — 13 — 414

Baby baby baby oh yeah baby oh oh yee yip yip yahoo — 13 — 420

© 1994 Bean a Rama Music

Figure 10.1. Lyric Sheet

BOUNCING AND COMPING

After these work tracks are recorded, the engineer and producer might want to compile (or comp) the best parts of each track. They will listen to each track section by section, or line by line. Then they will use the lyric sheet to map out the best parts of both tracks, and the engineer will bounce all these choice parts to one separate choice comp track, in this case, track 18. Figure 10.1.

Bouncing also occurs when the engineer combines two or more different tracks to one track. Once these tracks are combined on another track, the original tracks can be erased to open even more space. However, once separate tracks are combined on a single track, there is no undoing them.

When bouncing tracks encoded with noise reduction, leave them encoded, unless combining tracks. Keep very accurate records on the tracksheet regarding tracks with noise reduction.

CLEANING TRACKS

Once tracks have been bounced, the original tracks should be erased (simply called cleaned) before they are re-recorded. Of course, these tracks don't *have* to be cleaned. Any new program recorded on a track automatically erases the old program. But it is better to completely erase the old track and start fresh with a clean track, rather than chance hearing snippets of the old track come through, especially if there are a lot of punch-ins involved in the new track.

To clean tracks, rewind the tape to the top of the song and put the appropriate track in *record-ready*. Activate the VSO, and turn it all the up. Then press record. The track will erase, and it will take less time than letting the song play through at its normal speed. As the track is being erased, erase the track information on the tracksheet.

You must listen to the song as it plays at the increased speed, so you can press stop at the right time. You don't want to keep recording into the same track on the next song, which is not meant to be erased. Again, never erase anything without first checking with the engineer.

FLY-INS

A fly-in, also called a spin-in, is a section of a track or tracks lifted from one part of a song, and recorded elsewhere. For example, the background vocals on chorus 1 are great, and, to save time, the producer wants to use the same background vocals on all choruses. The engineer must lift the background vocal from the first chorus using the mixdown machine, and fly them into the rest of the choruses. Sometimes fly-ins originate elsewhere, such as when sound effects are added to a song. Here are some of the ways to fly something into a song:

- Bounce the fly-in, in this case a choice background vocal chorus, over to a mixdown machine. Wind the multitrack machine to the second verse. Manually synchronize both machines while re-recording the background vocals over to the multitrack machine.

- If the mixdown machine has a track for timecode, bounce the code over from the master with the fly-ins. Synchronize both machines, set the correct offset, then fly the choice chorus into the rest of the song.

- Load the fly-in into a sampler, and play the sampler into the rest of the choruses.

- Load the whole background vocal track into a computer with digital editing capabilities. Duplicate the first chorus into the rest of the choruses, synchronize the computer to the multitrack machine, and fly the track back into the song.

- Use a digital delay with a long delay time. Set the delay time to exactly the length from the start of the first chorus, to the start of the second chorus. However, this method might not always work.

When labeling fly-ins, mark down where they originated, and where and when they were added. If the fly-in tape is a DAT, there will not be enough space to write all this pertinent information on the small label, so write it in the daily log.

FLIPPING THE REEL

Analog tapes are sometimes flipped over to create a count in for a song where there is none. Flipping the reel is also sometimes used for that spacey reverse "Hendrix" effect. The tape is flipped over, and the backwards music is sent through an echo chamber and recorded. When the tape is flipped back again, the echo chamber has been recorded backwards.

Whatever reason the engineer has to flip the reel, always transport the tape to the end of the song, or all the way off the reel. Undo the spindles on both sides, and turn both reels over, with the take-up reel upside down on the supply side, and the supply reel upside down on the take-up side. The end of the song, or the reel, is now the beginning. All tracks now return on opposite channels. Track 24 returns in channel 1, track 23 returns in channel 2, etc.

Re-label the desk with the backwards tracks, double check the tracksheet, and listen to the section of tape before pressing *record*. Do not say to yourself "I don't need to re-write the strip out. Any idiot can count backwards from 24 to figure out which track is returning where." Well, you're reading hard learned advice from "any idiot." Write the strip out correctly. This is where it can be very easy to accidentally erase something important.

SLAVES

As tracks get used up, another way to create more space for recording is to make slaves. A slave of a song is simply a copy of a master. Tracks on the master tape are mixed down and, with a timecode, bounced over to another multitrack tape and used for additional recording. If for example, the master multitrack tape has nine tracks of drums, they might be bounced down to four or two tracks on the slave. All guitars and keyboards might be bounced to a pair of stereo tracks. This leaves many more tracks available for additional recording on the slave.

As the slave gets full, these guide tracks (tracks bounced over from the master tape) can be bounced again to a stereo mix on other tracks within the slave, or the slave and master can be synchronized, and the new tracks can be bounced into the master.

One might think it is best to record a good stereo mix from all tracks on the master over to the slave, and simply use this mix for monitor during all the overdubs. However, keeping some instruments on separate tracks gives the engineer a degree of flexibility during overdubs and rough mixes.

As these guide tracks get bounced down they may lose some of their inherent good sound. Of course, these guide tracks are not masters, but copies, and only used for monitor while recording overdubs. The master tracks are used for mixdown.

Slaves are not always made to open up space. They are also made:

• During a lengthy project to protect the integrity of master tapes. Tape continually crossing the heads may slowly cause signal degradation, so a slave may be used for overdubs. This keeps the master intact until mixdown.

• When additional recording takes place at another studio. The master stays in use at your studio, and a slave is sent off to be worked on elsewhere.

• Because some engineers like to record some instruments on analog tape for that certain analog sound, then transfer tracks over to a digital slave for the rest of the recording. A digital to digital copy is not a slave, but a clone.

• When many tracks of the same part are recorded, then all comped to a single or stereo tracks. A guitar or vocal slave may be made for a musician to record all his brilliant ideas while he comes up with a choice part.

The master and slave are synchronized (locked together), and the new choice tracks are either all bounced to one slave, all bounced to the master, or left on the slave. Three or more machines may be locked together, but this only occurs in the largest of sessions.

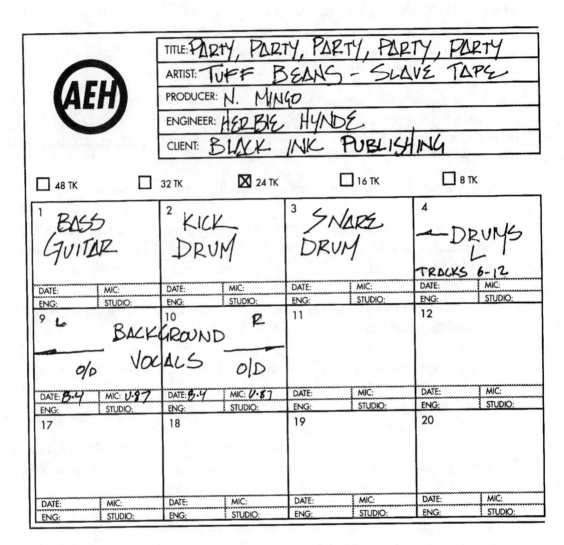

Figure 10.2. Slave Tracksheet

FINDING TAPE

Due to the expense of multitrack tape, reels containing outtakes from the basics may sometimes be re-used to make slaves. Search each outtake reel for sections of unedited tape longer than the length of the song being slaved.

DATE: 8.4	TAPE: 696	SPEED: ☒ 30 IPS ☐ 15 IPS ☐ DIGITAL
STUDIO: ☒ A ☐ B ☐ C		N. R.: ☐ DOLBY ☐ DBX ☐ _____
REEL: ⟨1 OF:		SAMPLING RATE: ☐ 48 K ☐ 44.1 K
TONES ON REEL M·1 ☐ HEAD ☒ TAIL		REF: 360 nWm = 0VU ☒ NAB ☐ IEC
ASSISTANT ENGINEER: A. READER		

☐ 4 TK | ☐ MASTER | ☐ SAFETY | ☒ SLAVE | ☐ CLONE

5 DRUMS — R TRACKS 6-12	6 15,19	7 KEYBOARDS & GUITARS 16,20	8 VOCAL ♯
DATE: — MIC:	DATE: — MIC:	DATE: — MIC:	DATE: — MIC:
ENG: — STUDIO:	ENG: — STUDIO:	ENG: — STUDIO:	ENG: — STUDIO:
13	14	15 TRUMPET SAXOPHONE O/D	16 TRUMPET HORNS O/D
DATE: — MIC:	DATE: — MIC:	DATE: 8·4 — MIC: 11·87	DATE: 8·4 — MIC: U·87
ENG: — STUDIO:	ENG: — STUDIO:	ENG: — STUDIO:	ENG: — STUDIO:
21	22	23 CLICK	24 TIME CODE
DATE: — MIC:	DATE: — MIC:	DATE: — MIC:	DATE: — MIC:
ENG: — STUDIO:	ENG: — STUDIO:	ENG: — STUDIO:	ENG: — STUDIO:

Erase all tracks on the section of the tape before the new song is recorded. The tape to be used for the slave should be totally blank. Again, check with the engineer before erasing any outtakes.

If, while making a slave, you see a splice on the tape go by, don't use that section of tape. Use sections of tape with no splices. As well, don't record music over tape that has contained tones, as the tone never fully erases.

Load the multitrack machine with the correct tape, and make out a slave track-sheet. Figure 10.2. Often the engineer will write out how he wants the tracks on a slave tracksheet, and leave the rest of the information for you to fill in. Write the session information as it is written on the master tracksheet, the only difference being the date. Chances are slim that the slave is made the same day as the basics are recorded. Clearly mark the tracksheet SLAVE 1.

Not all individual track information written on the master tracksheet needs to be duplicated on the slave tracksheet — just the instruments, and where they originated on the master tape.

When overdubs are recorded on the slave, document these new tracks with all pertinent information just like on the master reel tracksheet. Mark overdubs on the slave reel with a red dot, to avoid any confusion between new overdubs and guide tracks bounced from the master.

BUSSING AND PATCHING

When the slave reel is loaded and ready, route the individual master tracks over from the desk to the slave multitrack machine. According to this slave tracksheet, the engineer wants you to:

- Switch tracks 1 to 8, 23 (the click track) and 24 (the timecode track) to *record-ready*. This shows you the input of each track on the slave machine.

- Buss both bass tracks, 2 and 3, from the master onto track 1 on the slave.

- Patch the kick and snare drums from master tracks 4 and 5 directly to slave tracks 2 and 3. Buss the rest of the drums to tracks 4 and 5.

- Buss all the guitars and keyboards to tracks 6 and 7.

- Patch the vocal from track 18 on the master to track 8 on the slave.

- Patch the click from track 23 on the master to track 23 on the slave.

Assign all busses, set proper levels and panning, and perhaps add equalization and reverbs. Notice that individual one-to-one tracks, such as the vocal from the master, are patched straight across from one machine to the other, bypassing the bussing and processing at the desk. For a safe, reliable lockup, avoid printing anything loud on the tracks adjacent to the timecode. For a really safe, reliable lockup, try being a crooked politician.

TIMECODES

To synchronize various machines together in the studio, either SMPTE, or EBU timecodes are routinely recorded on one track of both the master and the slave. This timecode is like a 24-hour clock running hours, minutes, seconds and frames. When a synchronizer reads this timecode, it servo locks one machine to another. When the master is in motion, the slave chases and follows, with both machines reacting as one. Timecode is also used to program some musical instruments, such as some keyboards.

As well, timecode is sometimes used to track cue locations throughout the reel. Computer mixdown automation is also based on timecode. The computer reads the timecode track, and activates changes in the mix at specific pre-programmed times. Multitrack machines and video recorders are often locked for synchronizing music to video. The technical staff at your studio will be able to answer most of your questions. Understanding timecodes and their use can be challenging. I recommend that you learn more on the subject than is mentioned here.

HOUSE SYNC.

Most larger studios now have a house sync. generator, also called video black. House sync. is simply one master clock for the whole premises. This technology, borrowed from the video world, allows digital machines, synchronizers and timecode to run at exactly the same speed, or clock rate. All modern digital equipment now has an external sync. connectors located at the back of the unit.

All equipment should be set to *external sync.* This makes synchronization a breeze (theoretically.) With one studio standard, there should be no misunderstandings or errors when generating, printing and reading timecodes.

Offsets and Jam-Synchronization

An offset is created when one audio cue - with timecode, must be synchronized with another audio cue - with timecode. This produces a number that is the difference between these two audio cues. For example, if cue one (on the master reel) is at 00:05:30.00 and cue two (on the slave reel) is at 00:05:10.12, (Translation: 00 hours 05 minutes 10 seconds 12 frames.) this will produce an offset of -00:00:19.18. With this offset number entered in the synchronizer, the two audio cues will line up.

Often during the editing of analog tape, the recorded timecode becomes discontinuous. A new timecode needs to be regenerated, but referenced to the original timecode. The jam-sync function (available on most synchronizers) reads the timecode ahead of the first edit, then regenerates new continuous timecode on the remainder of the faulty timecode track. This procedure is also used to repair dropouts on the timecode track.

Before printing new timecode, set the timecode generator to start at one minute, or one hour, not at zero. Because the timecode is a 24-hour clock, the numbers restart the sequence after 23:59:59.29 (depending on the type of timecode) to 00:00:00.00. For example, you print timecode before the beginning of the song starting at 00:01:00.00. Later in the project, the client wants a longer introduction to the song. The timecode can't be re-recorded, so you must record one minute of additional code in before the existing code.

Because the timecode starts at 00:01:00.00, one minute of code can be recorded before the beginning of the song, then flow uninterrupted into the existing timecode as the song begins. If original timecode starts at 00:00:00.00, the timecode before it would be the ending of the previous 24-hour cycle. 23:59:59.29. This means the cycle would change within the song.

If one minute was jam-synced in ahead of the song, the code would start at 23:59:00.00, then flow over the end of the cycle, and start a new cycle within the song. If you press the locate button for the machine go to the beginning of the song, it will *fast-forward* to 23:59:00.00 of the new cycle, when it really should *rewind* to 23:59:00.00 of the previous cycle.

SYNCHRONIZATION AND TRANSFER

To record the house sync. reference timecode on the master and slave tapes, patch from the output of the generator into the input of the designated code tracks (often track 24.) Most synchronizers also have a timecode generator, reshaper (which reads the existing timecode, and reshapes it, or cleans it up) and regenerator (which reads the existing code, and completely regenerates new code.)

The input level on the VU meters should read approximately -7db. This level is a fair compromise between adjacent track crosstalk and enough level for the synchronizer to read the timecodes. If the code generator output level is different than -7db, patch the signal into a channel on the desk, and set the level to -7db. Always start the timecode well before the song's count-off to allow enough time for machines to lock.

If the master tape has no timecode, record the timecode on both tapes and make the transfer simultaneously. The following procedure assumes both machines have been properly aligned. To make the slave, follow these steps:

1) Transport the master tape to at least 10 to 15 seconds before the start of the song. Load the slave tape on the slave machine.

2) Patch the timecode generator into track 24 of the master tape and track 24 of the slave tape. Set the code generator to start at 00:01:00.00.

3) Press *record* on the master and slave machines. All appropriate tracks, 1 to 8, 23, and 24 on the slave machine, and track 24 on the master machine should light up.

4) Monitor the tracks from the slave tape at the desk, and let both machines run to beyond the ending of the song.

5) Stop both tapes, and rewind them to the beginning of the song. Set the parameters on the synchronizer to *chase* mode.

6) Press *play* on the master machine, and the slave machine should chase the master. This may take a few seconds at first as the synchronizer learns the servo curve.

7) Make sure they lock well before the beginning of the song by looking at the synchronizer. It will show you when both machines are locked.

8) As the two synchronized machines are playing back, solo two of the same tracks on the master and the slave, for example, the snare drum tracks. Put both tracks up the middle, not panned left and right. If the master and slave are locked, these tracks from both reels will flange with each other. This means success.

9) If needed, write down the new cue numbers on the slave tracksheet.

If timecode has previously been printed on the master tape, rewind the master tape to before the song, where the timecode begins. Use the synchronizer to regenerate this time code on the slave tape while making the transfer. If existing timecode on the master tape is inconsistent due to splices, re-striping the master may be impractical because the code may have been used for other slaves, midi, or cue locations. Ask the engineer if he wants you to re-print new continuous timecode over the imperfect timecode on the master tape, and fresh identical code simultaneously to the slave tape, or to regenerate the existing impractical code onto the slave tape.

SONG LAYOUT

If a master tape contains three songs, then the slave reel also should contain the slaves of the same three songs in the same order. If at all possible, keep the master and slave layouts consistent. However, some songs on the project may have no slaves while some songs may have many. Slaves tend to be made as the need arises. If a song does have more than one slave, place each slave on a separate reel, as the two slaves may need to be locked together.

Putting a slave reel on the master machine shows that the terms *slave* and *master* are just labels for functions. Two slaves can be locked together, or a slave tape can be put on the master machine, and the master tape on the slave machine. The process is simply one timecode chasing and locking to another. Some sessions refer to the tapes as the A tape, B tape, and C tape with none being classed as master or slave. Each reel simply holds different material. Some sessions will want to bring in additional machines, and even lock video and audio.

SAFETY MASTERS

Safety masters are direct track-to-track copies of master tapes, made to stay in the tape vault in case the master tapes are lost or damaged in transit. True, a safety is a copy of the master, and analog copies are a generation down, but safety masters are certainly usable if the master tapes are unavailable. Digital safety masters of digital masters are not copies at all, but clones — exactly the same as the master.

Although slaves and safety masters are used for different purposes, making a safety master, whether of a multitrack tape, or of a mix tape, uses a similar procedure to that of making a slave. For best results, come directly out of the XLR outputs on the back of the master machine and into the XLR inputs on the back of the safety machine. If this is not possible, make the appropriate patches at the patchbay. Patch all tracks directly across except the timecode track, which should be reshaped or regenerated.

For a direct copy of the master tape (copies are sometimes called dubs), all tracks on the safety tracksheet should match the master tracksheet. When you combine more than one track from the master tape to the safety, this tape ceases being a safety master, and becomes a slave.

On digital recorders, plug the appropriate digital dubbing cable, usually multi-pin, capable of transferring eight or twenty-four tracks at a time. Other cables are needed to allow the machines to talk to each other, including CTL/A-time, and timecode information. Select *digital* input on the slave/clone machine.

A photocopy of the master tracksheet can be used for this safety master. Hopefully this safety master will never need to be used, but if it is used, re-write the tracksheet in pencil before any additional recording. Label the box and the reel clearly to avoid any confusion.

If any tapes were recorded with noise reduction, it is not necessary to decode and encode to make the copy. Simply bypass the noise reduction, and patch straight across. The safety master will remain encoded with the noise reduction.

. . . .

Summary

Chapter Ten explained about what is expected of the assistant engineer while the overdubs are recorded:

- Changing reels and finding songs.

- Setting up the studio with a microphone, stand and headphones.

- Setting up the desk with new or previous sounds, and checking the signal flow for the overdub.

- Recording the overdub, bouncing, comping, flying in, and flipping the tape.

- Making slaves and safety masters, timecodes and synchronization.

CHAPTER ELEVEN

· ·

Mixdown

At some point in every project, there is a mixdown (usually called a mix.) Mixing is the process whereby all tracks, whether live or recorded, are combined, usually with signal processing such as equalization, limiting, reverbs, and delays typically to a pair of stereo tracks. Film soundtracks may be mixed to three, four, five and even six tracks. All final mixes are then assembled, often mastered, duplicated and distributed.

Mixing can take anywhere from a few moments, to a few hours to a few days. Big budget projects have been known to take weeks to mix one song, while jingles are usually recorded and mixed in a single day.

ROUGH MIXES

During a project, rough mixes (called roughs) are printed for everyone to take away from the studio and evaluate the tracks so far. They are often just a quick pass of the monitor mix and are printed on anything from a single cassette to a master mixdown machine. A full set of rough mixes might be made after basic tracks before all songs are completed, depending on how the engineer and producer prefer to work.

If you have the time, log all the rough mixes. The heartbreak of ruffitis has been known to occur during a final mix, when someone keeps referring back to a rough mix for certain sounds or effects that he feels are needed on the final mix. Writing down the few sends, returns, inserts and processing shouldn't take long, and it might come in very helpful during final mixes.

ROUGH MIX TAPE

Make a "rough mix tape," usually either DAT or ¼", containing all the current rough mixes. Replace or record over outdated mixes as each new song is rough mixed. Label each mix on the reel with the date and the most recent overdub. Perhaps record a short set of tones at the head of the tape.

If the speed of any song is changed with the multitrack machine's VSO, the overall length of the song will change. Remember this when recording over an older version of a song with a newer version at a different speed.

If the rough reel is a DAT, you may not want to record over older versions of rough mixes. An easier method, because of the ample space available on a DAT tape, is to put each current rough mix after the last one on tape, with the date, mix number, and index number on the label. Write mix details in the daily log.

WHEN YOU DO THE ROUGH MIXES

As with monitor mixes, if the engineer feels comfortable with the job you do, he may let you do the rough mixes. If he does, keep these mixes simple and basic. Use the same outboard equipment and settings that the engineer uses. Do a basic rough mix, nothing radical, just so everything can be heard. This is not the time to do the world's most partyin' dance mix. You should know approximately how the engineer likes things panned, so be consistent with him. Blend the most recent overdub with the rest of the tracks — don't make it the loudest thing in the mix. Remember, everyone on the project will hear your mixes.

FINAL MIXES

For the assistant engineer, a mixdown session is essentially the same as a basics session, because many of the same rules apply. Throughout the session, you will be setting up the outboard equipment, patching, changing and keeping track of all tapes, helping the engineer at the desk, and printing and logging the applicable information. The following are a few priorities for before, during, and after a final mix:

BEFORE THE MIX

- Arrive well ahead of the sessions scheduled start time so you can arrange for any rental equipment, special alignments or synchronization before the engineer arrives. The studio's technical department may need to be involved for the initial setup of equipment.

- Clean and stock the control room. Bring enough supplies, including cassettes, DATs, data disks (if used), mixing tape, tape labels, and other stationery.

- Keep all virgin mix tapes with their boxes close by and ready to be labeled. All virgin analog mix reels should be from the same batch.

- Zero the desk and add a fresh strip of white adhesive tape for the engineer to write on. Don't write it out, as he may want to change the layout of the tracks.

- Bring all equipment scheduled for the mix, such as rental equipment, floaters, and engineer's outboard into the room and correctly place and connect them. Turn on, clean, and align all tape machines, and test all inputs and outputs, sends and returns. If applicable, load the computer with the data disk containing all of the song information.

• Find the master multitrack tape with the song to be mixed. Load the multitrack machine and transport the tape to the beginning of the song. Activate any noise reduction or VSO needed. Load any slaves on their respective machines, making sure the synchronizer is reading the proper timecodes, any synchronizer offset is entered, and all tapes are locking correctly.

• Place the tracksheet and the cue sheet, if separate, on the desk facing the engineer.

SETTING UP THE MIXDOWN MACHINE

Load the mixdown machine with an exercised virgin mix tape and cue it up to the beginning of the tape. Then follow these steps:

• Switch the mixdown machines to *record-ready*. When any non-virgin tape other than the current mix tape is loaded on a mixdown machine, switch the machine out of *record-ready*.

• If mixes on your session are recorded directly to computer hard drive, set the input and output as you would a regular mixdown machine.

• Print alignment tones to the mixdown machine. The only difference between the multitrack tape tones and mix tape tones is the length of each tone needed. As you are probably only printing to two tracks, not a full multitrack tape, there is no need to print a full minute of each tone. Thirty seconds of each should be ample time. Print a set of tones for the mixes as described in Chapter Four, and keep these tones on reel 1.

Mixes are often printed to both analog and digital formats simultaneously, so the client can hear both after mixing, then decide which to use.

SETTING UP THE DAT MACHINE

In the recording studio, digital cassettes, simply called DATs, are becoming increasingly popular because of the high quality reliable results, ease of use, compact size, and decreasing prices. Virtually all mixing sessions today have a DAT machine running. Before printing mixes to DAT, print a set of tones as follows:

1) Exercise DAT cassettes the same as you would analog tapes. Load the tape, and fast-forward it all the way to the end, then rewind it back to the beginning.

2) Put the DAT machine in *record-ready,* then disengage the automatic indexing function. The automatic indexing function assigns one ID number to each musical passage. When the engineer presses "3" on the DAT machine, he should hear the third pass, not the third tone.

3) Set the desk oscillator output to 0 VU on the master meters, as described in Chapter Four.

4) Set the input meters on the DAT machine to your studio standard. Different studios may vary between a standard input level of somewhere between -12db to -20db = 0 VU. This allows 12 to 20db of headroom before clipping. When digital tape is clipped or overloaded, it doesn't distort, as analog tape does, it simply creates pure distortion. One clipped level can ruin an entire pass.

5) Reading A-time, or absolute (real) time on the DAT machine, record 15 seconds of blank tape, then record a 1khz. tone.

6) At 45 seconds, change the tone to 10khz.

7) At 1 minute 15 seconds, change the tone to 50hz.

8) At 1 minute 45 seconds, mute the input of the DAT machine and let the tape roll past the 2 minute mark, then stop the machine.

9) Restart the automatic indexing feature so the first mix to tape is indexed as "1."

10) DAT machines can show the input levels without being in *record-ready* mode. Don't leave the machine in *record-ready* or it might automatically go into record after a few minutes. The DAT machine is now ready to record.

Before unwanted tracks are erased on the multitrack tape, audio and timecode tracks are routinely dumped to the DAT. Then, if any part needs retrieving, the multitrack machine is synchronized to the DAT machine, and the track is bounced back into the master tape. Being able to retrieve everything recorded during the project lifts the burden of hearing the age old statement, "What do you mean you erased it?"

DURING THE MIX

During the mix, watch that all the equipment is acting and reacting how the engineer wants it — not necessarily correctly, but how he wants it. For example, some engineers like to record very hot to tape. If the input meters on the mix machines look too high or low, bring it to his attention before the recording begins.

Listen for stray sounds, or for tracks that are on but should be off, or tracks that are off that should be on. To remove any unwanted noise, such as a singer coughing, or a string buzzing, the engineer often mutes the specific channel before the unwanted noise begins, or he simply erases the noise. However, at this stage of the project, accidentally erasing something important on the master tape would be distressing. Having to go back and re-record something could be a blow to the session. This is the time for you and the engineer to be extra careful. There tends to be a load lifted off everyone's shoulders when all the tracks are recorded.

PATCHING

Make a list describing all patches being made, including crosspatches, inserts, busses, sends and returns, and include all outboard equipment being used. Whenever a patch is added, changed, or revised, note the change on the list. Leave the patch list on the desk where the engineer can see it and understand it at a glance. Ater the mix, use the list to check off each patch as you remove it, just to double check that all patches are correctly logged.

Crosspatching

The layout of tracks on the tracksheet is not always how the engineer wants them to appear at the desk while mixing. Crosspatching (or multing) allows the re-routing of a multitrack return normally returning in one channel line input, over to another. Tracks are crosspatched to different channels for many different reasons, including:

- To split tracks containing more than one instrument for individual processing. For example in Figure 11.4. track 15, which contains two different instruments in two different sections of the song, is patched into channels 16 and 27. Each channel can be processed separately, with one muted while the other plays.

- To group, or re-arrange the returns for familiarity. For example, the engineer may always prefer the lead vocal track to return in channel 24, no matter where it appears on tape.

- To arrange tracks from the slave machine so they return with the rest of the instruments. For example, if the choice background vocal tracks on the slave tape are on tracks 8 and 9, these might be patched over to where the other vocals are returning on the desk.

- Some desks have certain channels that house better equalization modules than the rest of the channels on the desk. The engineer may want specific tracks, such as vocals, in these channels because of their superior sound qualities.

When crosspatching, make sure all tracks from the multitrack machine are patched into the desk. Sometimes a small part recorded late at night, or early in the project may be overlooked. Maybe put a check mark on each track on the tracksheet as each patch is made. The tracksheet will be covered with check marks, but so what? After the mix, the tracksheet will no longer be needed.

Additional Patching

- After patching in a piece of outboard equipment, label the outboard with a small strip of adhesive tape, stating the send into it and where it returns on the desk. The engineer wants to see, with a quick look around the control room, what each piece of equipment is being used for. During a mix, label all the equipment. You might even want to label his can of soda. All too often I've heard someone in a session ask, "Is this your soda or mine?"

- Use the enclosed delay chart, Figure 11.1. to write the exact ¼, ⅓, and ½ note delay times from the BPM as written on the tracksheet (fig. 6.2.) The engineer will use these numbers to set his delay and echo pre-delay times of the song. If you don't have the BPM, listen to the song and time exactly 10 seconds, then multiply the beats by 6. For example, 15 beats in a 10 second period, multiplied by 6 is 120 BPM. According to fig. 11.1. the ¼ note for 120 BPM is 500 ms.

- Often, samples are used during a mix. Right after loading the sample, note the input level of the sampler in case the sample gets lost and needs re-loading. This input level might need to be changed to a different level to get the sample to correctly trigger. Of course, also note the specific sample or samples used.

- Many pieces of outboard equipment have internal storage capacity. Once the engineer sets the parameters, write them down on the setup sheet, then store them internally. If the unit accidentally gets unplugged, or if a future re-mix is imminent, the settings are easily retrievable.

  Also, if the engineer is limited in outboard equipment, he may need different settings for different parts of a song. For example, you may need to change the settings on a digital reverb for the choruses, then go back to the original setting for the rest of the song. With each setting stored internally, the programs can be changed with the press of one button. Of course, this change is needed every time a mix is printed.

- Clean the heads on the multitrack machine right before printing the first mix.

DELAY CHART IN MILLISECONDS

BPM	1/4	1/4 TRIP	1/8	1/8 TRIP	1/16	1/16 TRIP	1 BAR	2 BARS	4 BARS	8 BARS
80	750.0	500.0	375.0	250.0	187.5	125.0	3.000	6.111	12.000	24.000
81	740.7	493.8	370.4	246.9	185.2	123.5	2.963	5.926	11.852	23.704
82	731.7	487.8	365.9	243.9	182.9	122.0	2.927	5.854	11.707	23.415
83	722.9	481.9	361.4	241.0	180.7	120.5	2.892	5.783	11.566	23.133
84	714.3	476.2	357.1	238.1	178.6	119.0	2.857	5.714	11.429	22.857
85	705.9	470.6	352.9	235.3	176.5	117.6	2.824	5.647	11.294	22.588
86	697.7	465.1	348.8	232.6	174.4	116.3	2.791	5.581	11.163	22.326
87	689.7	459.8	344.8	229.9	172.4	114.9	2.759	5.517	11.034	22.069
88	681.8	454.5	340.9	227.3	170.5	113.6	2.727	5.455	10.909	21.818
89	674.2	449.4	337.1	224.7	168.5	112.4	2.697	5.393	10.787	21.574
90	666.7	444.4	333.3	222.2	166.7	111.1	2.667	5.333	10.667	21.333
91	659.3	439.6	329.7	219.8	164.8	109.9	2.637	5.275	10.549	21.099
92	652.2	434.8	326.1	217.4	163.0	108.7	2.609	5.217	10.435	20.870
93	645.2	430.1	322.6	215.1	161.3	107.5	2.581	5.161	10.323	20.645
94	638.3	425.5	319.1	212.8	159.6	106.4	2.553	5.106	10.213	20.426
95	631.6	421.1	315.8	210.5	157.9	105.3	2.526	5.053	10.105	20.211
96	625.0	416.1	312.5	208.3	156.3	104.2	2.500	5.000	10.000	20.000
97	618.6	412.4	309.3	206.2	154.6	103.1	2.474	4.948	9.897	19.794
98	612.2	408.2	306.1	204.1	153.1	102.0	2.449	4.898	9.796	19.592
99	606.1	404.0	303.0	202.0	151.5	101.0	2.424	4.848	9.697	19.394
100	600.0	400.0	300.0	200.0	150.0	100.0	2.400	4.800	9.600	19.200
101	594.1	396.0	297.0	198.0	148.5	99.0	2.376	4.752	9.505	19.010
102	588.2	392.2	294.1	196.1	147.1	98.0	2.354	4.706	9.412	18.824
103	582.5	388.3	391.3	194.2	145.6	97.1	2.330	4.660	9.320	18.641
104	576.9	384.6	288.5	192.3	144.2	96.2	2.308	4.615	9.231	18.462
105	571.4	381.0	285.7	190.5	142.9	95.2	2.286	4.571	9.143	18.286
106	566.0	377.4	283.0	188.7	141.5	94.3	2.264	4.528	9.057	18.113
107	560.7	373.8	280.4	186.9	140.2	93.5	2.243	4.486	8.972	17.944
108	555.6	370.4	277.8	185.2	138.9	92.6	2.222	4.444	8.889	17.778
109	550.5	367.0	275.2	183.5	137.6	91.7	2.202	4.404	8.807	17.616
110	545.5	363.6	272.7	181.8	136.4	90.9	2.192	4.364	8.727	17.455
111	540.5	360.4	270.3	180.2	135.1	90.1	2.162	4.324	8.649	17.297
112	535.7	357.1	267.9	178.6	133.9	89.3	2.143	4.286	8.571	17.143
113	531.0	354.0	265.5	177.0	132.7	88.5	2.124	4.248	8.496	16.991
114	526.3	350.9	263.2	175.4	131.6	87.7	2.105	4.211	8.421	16.842
115	521.7	347.8	260.9	173.9	130.4	87.0	2.087	4.174	8.348	16.696
116	517.2	344.8	258.6	172.4	129.3	86.2	2.069	4.138	8.276	16.552
117	512.8	341.9	256.4	170.9	128.2	85.5	2.051	4.103	8.205	16.410
118	508.5	339.0	254.2	169.5	127.1	84.7	2.034	4.068	8.136	16.271
119	504.2	336.1	252.1	168.1	126.1	84.0	2.017	4.034	8.067	16.134
120	500.0	333.3	250.0	166.7	125.0	83.3	2.000	4.000	8.000	16.000
121	496.8	331.5	248.0	165.5	123.9	82.7	1.984	3.968	7.936	15.872
122	492.5	327.9	246.3	163.9	123.0	81.9	1.962	3.936	7.872	15.744
123	488.2	325.3	244.2	162.6	122.1	81.3	1.952	3.904	7.808	15.616
124	484.0	322.6	242.0	161.3	121.3	80.6	1.936	3.872	7.744	15.488
125	480.1	319.9	240.1	159.6	120.0	79.8	1.920	3.840	7.680	15.360
126	475.9	317.3	238.2	158.6	119.2	79.3	1.904	3.808	7.616	15.232
127	472.1	314.6	236.9	157.3	118.4	78.6	1.888	3.776	7.552	15.104
128	469.5	312.6	234.5	156.3	117.2	78.1	1.876	3.752	7.504	15.008
129	465.0	309.9	232.5	154.9	116.2	77.4	1.860	3.720	7.440	14.880
130	462.0	307.9	231.0	153.9	115.5	76.9	1.848	3.696	7.392	14.784

Figure 11.1. Delay Chart

PRINTING THE MIX

- Just as you checked the record alignment of each analog multitrack reel before recording basics, check the record alignment of each virgin analog mix reel as it is loaded.

- While printing the mix, use the input/output button on the mixdown machine to compare the input levels with the output levels. If the input levels are different than the output levels, the alignment may be off.

- Always be aware of where the tape is parked before pressing *record*. Nothing important should get erased.

- If a tape slap echo is being used, clean the heads on the slap machine before recording the mix, and make sure there is enough tape left on the reel to last throughout the song. Tape slap is an older method of delay using a mixdown machine with a varispeed. This method of delay is rarely used today due to the abundance of digital delays.

- If there is a section that may have overloaded the tape during recording, note the counter number. When the pass is complete, rewind to the spot and listen to it using headphones.

- As in recording basics, write down the slate number for each mix on a takesheet.

- As printing to the mix machine begins, note where on the tape the slate is, and where the song starts. If you need to stop and rewind to record over the last pass, keep the original slate and tell the engineer. Most machines have a RTZ (return to zero) button, or number storage function that can be used when shuttling the tapes. When the RTZ button is pressed, the tape machine rewinds to zero on the tape counter. Don't record over previous passes unless the producer or engineer specifically tells you.

- Write the DAT machine's automatic index number and the absolute time of each mix on the DAT label.

- Even with computer mixdown automation, manual moves on the desk are sometimes needed. For example, a send needs to be turned up for one snare hit. Put a tiny piece of red adhesive tape on the specific send on the snare channel, so the engineer knows at a glance which knob to turn up.

- Don't stop the tape until the engineer tells you. If the ending of a song is cut off, such as the ending of a fade, too much time may be wasted editing on a new fade.

- Define the differences between mixes clearly. Often, without talking to you, the producer and engineer will discuss running a pass with, for instance, more bass guitar. Write this on a takesheet or tape label with any other differences between mixes.

- Keep complete track of all mixes, incomplete mixes, outtakes and everything else printed to tape. You need to know exactly where everything is when the editing and assembly begins.

- Before removing any DAT tape from the machine, rewind the tape to the beginning. This eliminates the possibility of the machine's mechanisms eating the tape in the middle of anything important.

EDITING THE MIX

Edits on the mix tape are the same as edits on the multitrack tape. Every piece removed from the master mixes must be labeled for easy retrieval. There may eventually be many mixes of a song, such as the single mix, the album mix, the extended mix, the 12" mix, the dance mix, etc.

For a jingle, many different versions may also be needed, for instance long versions, short versions, versions with backing vocals, without backing vocals, donuts, etc. All need to be labeled and organized so that any mix can be easily found. Time schedules on jingles do not allow for extra time to hunt around looking for lost pieces of music.

CASSETTES/COPIES

Throughout the project, the people in the session may want to take copies of the day's work home. The engineer rough mixes the song to a mixdown machine, then you make the copies to everyone's cassette. Each person usually gets a cassette, and this cassette is updated daily with the newest rough mixes of each song. Making copies of the day's work is a staple of your job. You make the copies, update the labels and give the cassettes to their respective owner. You get the cassettes back during the next session, cue them up, and record that sessions rough mixes.

Sometimes, at the end of a long session, when all that's left is a quick cleanup then home to bed, the producer mentions he needs 10 cassette copies, each with the songs in a different order — and he needs them first thing tomorrow morning. The first temptation is to pummel him with the closest dull object, but you realize the closest dull object is the bass player. You must stay and make the copies.

Cassette Machines

Most studios have at least one permanently mounted cassette machine normalled to the output of the desk. When several copies need to be made, either additional cassette machines have to be brought in, or many passes must be made to the limited number of available machines. When making cassette copies, remember these points:

• When more cassette machines are brought in for additional copies, they need to be connected to the patchbay. Consult with the technical department before plugging RCA unbalanced cassette machines into the balanced XLR mix buss at the desk.

- Split the output of the master machine at the patchbay with a mult. (a signal splitter at the patchbay.) Send signal from the output of one mixdown machine to the mult, then into the inputs of three or four cassette machines. This way, many copies can be made at once.

- Sometimes music from the copies may leak into the main studio monitor buss, so don't make copies when a master mix is being printed to a mixdown machine. This leakage may inadvertently be printed onto the master mix. However, if the cassette machines in your studio record leakage, ask the technical staff to look into it. This is a grounding problem.

- Designate one specific cassette machine for each person in the session. All of his tapes will be made on that machine for the duration of the project. As each machine has its own variable equalization and speed characteristics, these differences might show up when songs are recorded on different cassette machines. If the settings are left the same, the recordings should remain consistent from one day to the next.

  When the tape machines settings cannot physically be left the same throughout the project due to other sessions, write down each machine's parameters, levels, and whose tape is made on it. Return to these settings before the next session.

- If someone in the session owns a machine, always use it for his copies. He will want his copies recorded and played back on the same machine. What the hey, use his cables as well.

- When making many copies, start making them well before the end of the session. Then no one has to wait around for his copy after the session.

- If this is not possible, and all copies are made after the session, do them in order of importance. Make the producer's copy first, then a copy for the main person in the band, then a copy for the engineer. The drummer is often last. You don't get one.

Virgin Cassettes

Before opening a new cassette, check with the producer. In most studios, cassettes cost about the same as a night at the Hilton. He may not want to spend the extra money. After opening a fresh tape for someone, mark his name on the tape and the case label. Cassettes are often tossed around, left behind, lost, or simply mixed up, so with each tape properly labeled, the owner is easily identified.

Non-Virgin Cassettes

If not recording on virgin cassettes, gather everyone's tape and ask each owner where on the tape he wants the newest copy. When someone doesn't have his tape with him, you may have to make a new one. Occasionally, a musician will give you a cassette of unknown origin and say, "Just put the copy on here, mate, record over what's there." Try to discourage this, as the tape will probably make a poor copy. He might return the next day, complaining of the poor job the engineer is doing.

Make sure there is enough space on the cassette for a complete pass. If both sides are full, open a new tape, after asking the engineer. Load the tape in its respective machine and put the empty case on or next to it. Correctly cue the tape up to record the copy, then switch the machine to *record-ready*. Mark all new cassettes on the work order.

Setting Levels

Once the tape is correctly cued up and the machine is in *record-ready*, check the input levels. The input will be from one of two sources: either from a master mixdown machine, or live from the desk's main buss output. When setting levels:

- If the signal originates from a master mixdown machine, make the correct patches. Double check that left stays left and right stays right.

- If the signal originates from the desk's main buss output, the input to the cassette machine is probably normalled from the desk.

- If the signal originates from the desk's main buss output, and the cassette machines are patched from a master mixdown machine, their normal input from the desk is defeated. To regain the normal, don't pull all the input patches from each cassette machine. At the patchbay, pull the output patches from the master mixdown machine, and patch them to the main output from the desk. This will send the main desk output buss to the inputs of the cassette machines.

- Check with the technical department to determine each cassette machines' maximum peak level for recording. With the variety of cassette machines and brands of tape available today, each machine should be set up for optimum performance.

- Match the equalization settings from the tape's label onto the machine's equalization parameters.

- Set the levels while the engineer is doing the mix. Don't wait until he is ready to record to check the input level to the machines. When he is ready to record, the tapes should be too.

- When setting levels, use the loudest section from the source. Peak levels should periodically hit the red on the VU meter. The ideal level is hot, but not so hot it distorts the signal.

- Record a portion of the song, then rewind the tape. Use headphones to listen to the recording, making sure it is being recorded properly, with good levels, and no significant loss of signal. Then re-cue the tape to the correct spot.

- The engineer may mix a song louder on one day than on the previous day, so check the levels for every song. This keeps all levels on tape consistent.

Recording

Whenever recording any cassettes to be taken away from the studio, keep the spaces between the songs as short as possible. Anything over seven or eight seconds is too long. If you start the tape too late, and didn't get the complete intro of a song, ask the engineer to start over. Let no false starts go by on cassette copies.

Watch the input levels during recording. If any levels seem unusual during the pass, note the counter numbers. After the pass, rewind to the loudest section and, using headphones, listen for distortion. Check that the song is complete, and not cut off at the beginning or end. If the engineer presses stop on the multitrack machine, rewinds and starts the mix over, stop all cassettes and cue them up again.

When all copies are complete, rewind the tape to the beginning of the first song copied. The producer should be able to jump in his car, pop the tape in the machine, and hear latest versions.

Labeling The Tape

When labeling cassettes and DATs, use studio labels, not the ones included in the tape itself. Leave no doubt as to where the tape originated. Put all the necessary information on the label as neatly as possible. Figure 11.2. This label should include:

- The name of each song, its indexing or location on the tape, the date, and if there is room, the last overdub recorded so the listener knows how current the rough mix is. If anyone needs more information on a specific version of a song, look at the date on the tape, and refer to your daily log for complete details.

- Bias and equalization settings of the tape and machine.

- The name of the person who owns the tape.

- The name of the artist and the contents, such as "rough mixes," along the spine. Cassettes and DATs containing the final assembled mixes should have typed labels. These tapes are copies of the final masters and must look as professional as possible. Remove the safety tabs on all master tapes to avoid erasure.

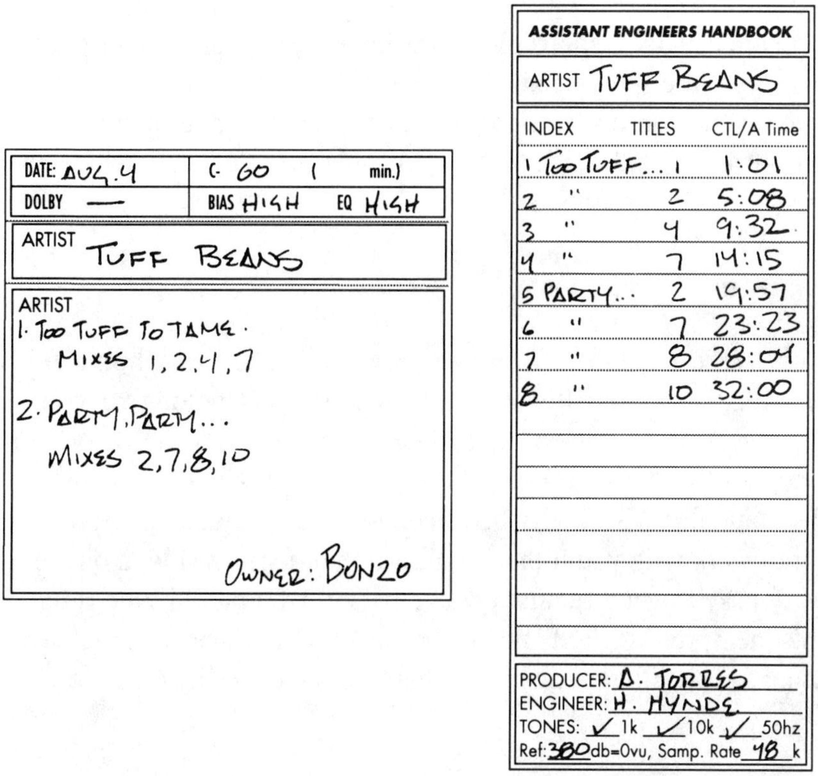

Figure 11.2. Cassette and DAT Label

THE COPY ROOM

Most larger studios have a designated room where all the tape copies are made. When many copies are needed, using the control room would tie up valuable studio time. If the studio does many jingles, a copy room is necessary as many copies of different formats and lengths are needed daily. The size of a copy room can vary from small with two machines, to a large fully staffed room, with walls of machines for mass duplication.

Because many different formats come through the studio, the copy room should contain all the proper machines to fit any needs, including digital and analog formats. Multitrack tape copies, such as safety masters and slaves, tend to be made in the control rooms.

You are usually responsible for making the copies of tapes that leave the studio. These tapes are sent to radio and television stations, record companies, managers, jingle houses, production companies, etc. Every tape leaving the studio must be properly assembled, leadered (if applicable), labeled, and double checked for accuracy before being sent out.

Your Personal Collection

Don't record copies of any sessions and take them home for your listening pleasure. First, it is illegal. Those songs don't belong to you, the studio, the producer, or the engineer. They belong to the band, the record company, the ad agency, or the financial backer. Second, if it falls into the wrong hands, such as a radio station, it will finally be traced to your studio, and then to you. No one will want to work with you if they think that their tapes will land on the streets. Third, It is very easy to get a reputation as a person who takes home rough mixes. No one wants their project heard outside the studio until it's been completed. They want the listener to enjoy the music to its fullest, not half finished.

AFTER THE MIX

DOCUMENTING THE MIX

Songs are often re-mixed if the original mix is unsatisfactory. A mix is logged so that all the mix settings can be returned to at any time in the future. Settings on all equipment used are re-set exactly, and the engineer either repairs the questionable parts and re-prints the mix, or he continues mixing the song until everyone is satisfied. Use setup sheets to write down the mix correctly.

MIX SETUP SHEETS

Setup sheets that are used to write down the mixes tend to be more in-depth than setup sheets used to write down individual sounds (fig. 9.1.) due to the amount of equipment involved. Every channel, patch, and setting must be logged precisely and clearly. One small error may mean a significant change in the mix.

If the engineer is mixing one song per session, the mix can usually be logged after the session ends. However, if more than one song is being mixed in a single session, begin the logging well before the mix is ready to be printed. The session shouldn't have to wait while you log the mix.

My rule of thumb is, start logging the mix when the computer mixdown automation gets turned on — if the studio has computer mixdown automation. This usually means the actual sounds are set, and the engineer wants to concentrate on the individual channel mutes, pans and levels.

Final mixes on large projects will always need to be logged. Some mixes, such as jingles, are rarely logged, due to lack of time. Most studios have a system in place that all the assistants use. The setup sheet is broken down into three basic sections: session information, patching, and outboard equipment.

Session Information

All the information regarding the mix not written anywhere else is written here. Figure 11.4. It includes:

- The date, artist, producer, engineer, assistant, client, tape speed, varispeed, offsets between machines, master or slave information, alignment and timecode infor-mation, and formats. The specific studio within the premises, such as studio A or B, is also noted here.

- The name and number of the song and specific mix logged. If there are 10 mixes of a certain song, settings of equipment may get slightly changed between the printing of mix 1 and mix 10. Each change needs to be logged.

- Any section of the desk not retained in the computer, such as the master send and return levels, desk compression and maybe subgroups.

- The specific multitrack and mixdown machines used. Larger studios may have many machines, all used in different sessions and situations. Different machines, even the same make and model, may have slight variations in sound reproduction.

With computer recall, the logging of the desk settings is as easy as pressing a key on the computer. The computer then stores the settings from each channel of the desk onto a data disk. Without computer recall, the desk settings will need to be logged manually. The setting of every channel, every knob, and every fader needs to be written down. However, this system is only accurate to a point. The engineer understands this, and will probably use the setup as a starting point for the re-mix.

Titles and numbers appearing on the computer should correspond to the tape labels and setup sheets. All mixes must be numbered on the computer data disk with cross-references to the setup sheets.

Patching

All patches, including their origin and destination, need to be logged. Figure 11.3. These include:

- Crosspatches. Write the track number from the master or slave, its input to the desk, and the name of the track as it appears on the strip. Compare the layout of the instruments on the tracksheet (fig. 6.2.) to the layout of the tracks on the desk during mixdown. Figure 11.4. This is how the instrument layout of the desk appears for the mix.

- Sends and effects returns. These are noted on both the setup sheet, and on the equipment's faceplate. For example, notice that send 3 is being sent into a harmonizer, then returning into stereo return #3. The "sends" section of the setup sheet shows where the sends originated, and where the unit is returning.

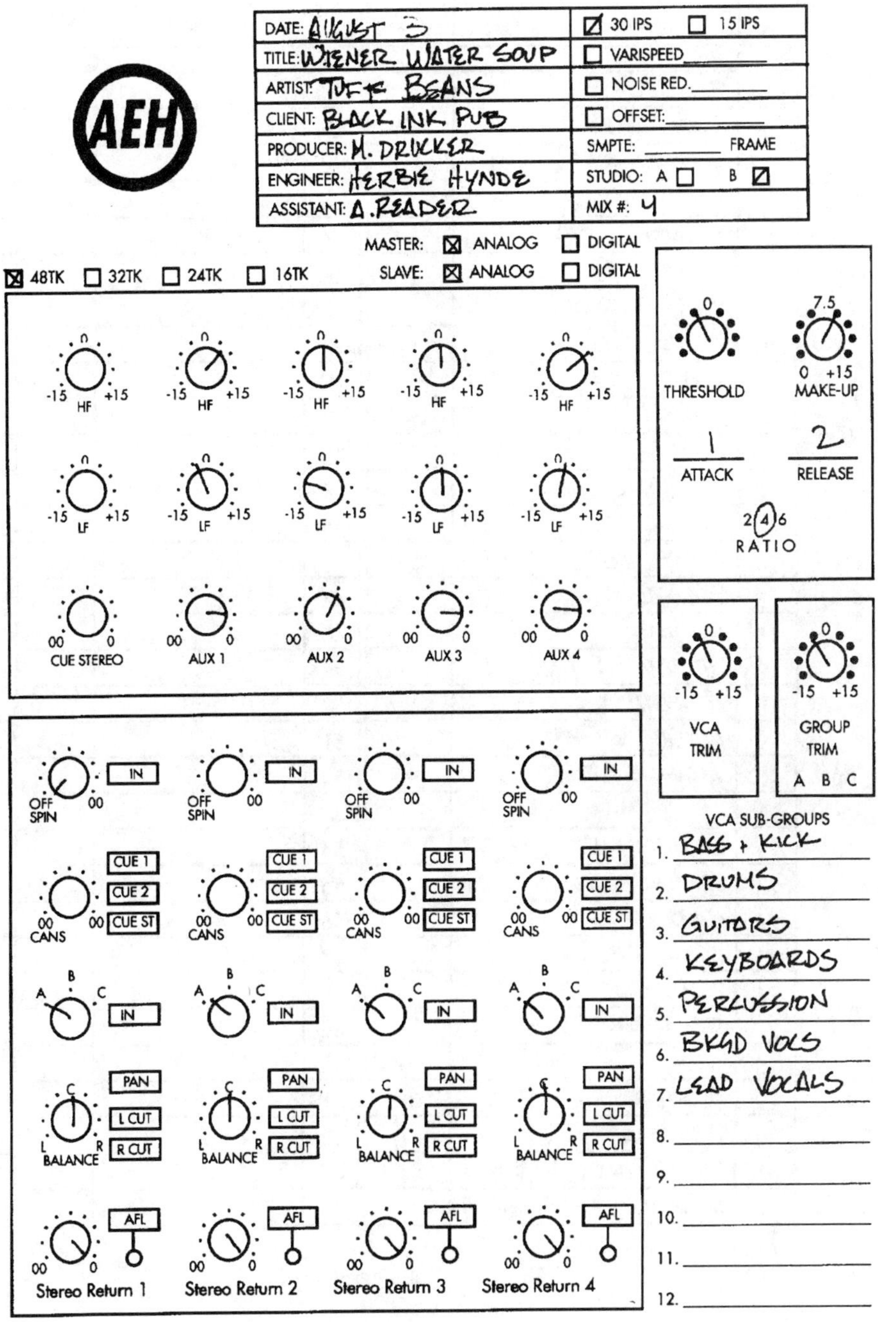

Figure 11.3. Session Information

CROSS-PATCHING

LINE IN	PROGRAM	SOURCE TRACK	TAPE MON IN	LINE IN	PROGRAM	SOURCE TRACK	TAPE MON IN
1	BASS AMP	2		33			
2	BASS DIRECT	3		34			
3	KICK DRUM	4		35			
4	KICK SAMPLE	Buss 3		36			
5	SNARE DRUM	5		37			
6	SNARE SAMPLE	Buss 4		38			
7	HIGH HAT	6		39			
8	TOMS L	7		40			
9	TOMS R	8		41			
10	CYMBALS L	9		42			
11	CYMBALS R	10		43			
12	AMBIANCE L	11		44			
13	AMBIANCE R	12		45			
14	HORNS L	SLAVE 15		46			
15	HORNS R	SLAVE 16		47			
16	GUITAR 1	15		48			
17	GUITAR 1 DBL	17		49			
18	GUITAR 2	16		50			
19	ACOUSTIC GTR 1	17		51			
20	ACOUSTIC GTR 2	22		52			
21				53			
22	BACKGROUND VOCS 1	SLAVE 9		54			
23	BACKGROUND VOCS 2	SLAVE 10		55			
24	LEAD VOCAL	18		56			
25	KEYBOARDS L	19		57			
26	KEYBOARDS R	20		58			
27	TAMBOURINE	15		59			
28				60			
29	FLANGER L	Buss 1		61			
30	FLANGER R			62			
31	DIGITAL DELAY 1	Buss 6		63			
32	DIGITAL DELAY 2	Buss 7		64			

Figure 11.4. Patching

SENDS

SENDS	EFFECT	RETURNS
1	DELAY #3 → ECHO CHAMBER #1	STEREO RETURN #1
2	DELAY #4 → ECHO CHAMBER #2	STEREO RETURN #2
3	HARMONIZER	STEREO RETURN #3
4		
5		
6		
CUE L	STEREO DELAY L	STEREO RETURN #4 L
CUE R	STEREO DELAY R	STEREO RETURN #4 R

INSERTS

INS. OUT		INS. IN
2	LIMITER #1 → EQUALIZER #1	2
3	LIMITER #2 → EQUALIZER #2	3
4	EQUALIZER #3	4
6	EQUALIZER #4	6
12	NOISE GATE #1	12
13	NOISE GATE #2	13
16	LIMITER #3	16
24	DE-ESSER → LIMITER #4	24

BUSSING

BUSS	EFFECT	RETURN
1	FLANGER	LINE INPUTS 29,30
2		
3	NOISE GATE #3 → KICK SAMPLE	LINE INPUT 4
4	NOISE GATE #4 → SNARE SAMPLE	LINE INPUT 6
5		
6	DIGITAL DELAY #1	LINE IN 31
7	DIGITAL DELAY #2	LINE IN 32
8		
9		
10		
11		
12	TRIGGER TO NOISE GATE 1	
13	TRIGGER TO NOISE GATE 2	
14		
15		
16		
17		
18		
19		
20		
21		
22		
23		
24		
25		
26		
27		
28		
29		
30		
31		
32		

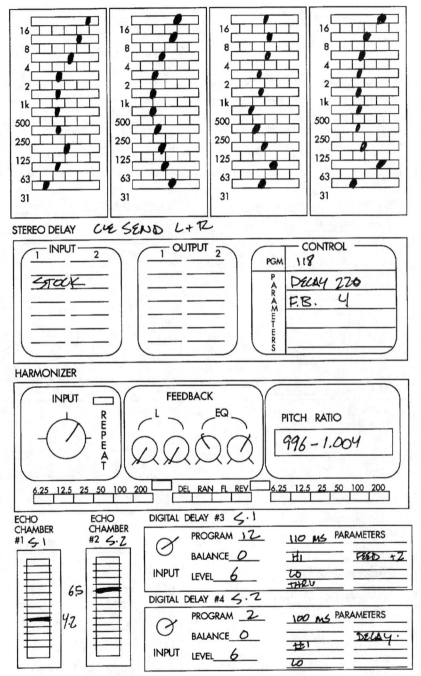

Figure 11.5. Outboard Equipment

NOISE GATE #1 _INSERT 12_   NOISE GATE #2 _INSERT 13_

EXT/INT		GATE/DUCK		KEY/GATE/BYPASS		STEREO LINK	EXT/INT		GATE/DUCK		KEY/GATE/BYPASS
LF	HF	THRES	ATT	HOLD DECAY RANGE			LF	HF	THRES	ATT	HOLD DECAY RANGE

NOISE GATE #3 _Buss 3_   NOISE GATE #4 _Buss 4_

EXT/INT		GATE/DUCK		KEY/GATE/BYPASS	STEREO LINK	EXT/INT		GATE/DUCK		KEY/GATE/BYPASS
LF	HF	THRES	ATT	HOLD DECAY RANGE		LF	HF	THRES	ATT	HOLD DECAY RANGE

DIGITAL DELAY #1 _Buss 6_   DIGITAL DELAY #2 _Buss 7_

DELAY X2	LEVEL	FEEDBACK	FILTER	PHASE	OUTPUT MIX	SET MODE	DELAY (ms)	MANUAL DEPTH WAVEFORM RATE
	INPUT	HI CUT	FB INV	DLY INV	INPUT DELAY	OC RPT	260	DELAY X5 X15 VCO-SWEEP

DELAY X2	LEVEL	FEEDBACK	FILTER	PHASE	OUTPUT MIX	SET MODE	DELAY (ms)	MANUAL DEPTH WAVEFORM RATE
	INPUT	HI CUT	FB INV	DLY INV	INPUT DELAY	OC RPT	263	DELAY X5 X15 VCO-SWEEP

SAMPLER _Busses 3/4_ _SNARE #13_ _KKK #17_

	INPUT	REGEN	DELAY	HARM
IN: Sep / Mix OUT: Sep / Mix				
A	.2	—	1.8	—
B	10	—	1.6	—
OUTPUT	VSO	SPEED	DEPTH	

LIMITER #1 _INSERT #2_

			ATTACK 2
7	5		
IN	OUT	REL	RATIO 4

LIMITER #2 _INSERT #3_

			ATTACK 2
6	2		
IN	OUT	REL	RATIO 4

FLANGER _Buss 1_

LIMITER #3 _INSERT #16_

			ATTACK 0
8	7		
IN	OUT	REL	RATIO 5

DE ESSER _Buss 24_

.5 .1	2 10	0 100%	.5 10 hz	DRY Td
KHZ				

LIMITER #4 _Buss 24_

			ATTACK 6
8	7		
IN	OUT	REL	RATIO 2

- Individual channel inserts, along with the equipment patched into each point. For example, in channel 2 the signal flows out of the insert point, into a limiter, into an equalizer, and then finally back into the insert return.

- Bussing, or group outputs. During mixing, busses often send signal from individual channels to outboard effects. For example, buss 1 on channel 3 is pressed. Channel 3, the kick drum, is being sent to the sampler which, in this example, holds the kick drum sample, then returns to line input 4. Channel 3 is the only channel on the desk with buss 1 pressed, as the kick drum track should be the only channel triggering the kick drum sample.

Outboard Equipment

Log the settings of each piece of outboard equipment by using a copy of the faceplate. Figure 11.5. As mentioned in Chapter Nine, most equipment manuals come with a template of the unit's faceplate. Photocopy this template and use it to write down the settings of the unit.

Sometimes all the information can be logged correctly without a photocopy of the faceplate. For example, a limiter with only a few dials can be simply written down with the actual numbers, such as "Input 7.2, Output 5.5," without needing an illustration of the unit. Yet again, whatever system is in use at your studio is the correct system to use. Included in this section of the setup sheet is:

- Everything about the actual unit. Log the faceplate, the inputs and outputs, all the internal settings, any controls on the rear of the unit, and include outboard equipment patched in but deactivated.

- The specific piece of outboard equipment used in the mixdown. For example, if the studio has eight identical equalizers, the engineer will want the same ones used on the re-mix. Notice on the setup sheet, inserts 2 and 3 house equalizers 1 and 2.

- The send, return or insert point used, as a cross-reference with the patching section.

If you have free access to a photocopy machine, you could create one master mix sheet, and simply re-use it. When the settings for the mix are correctly written down (in pencil), photocopy the complete setup sheet, making sure everything is legible. This copy is kept and used for the re-mix. Erase all the settings on the master sheet, and re-use it, updating it with the new mix information. As engineers tend to be fairly consistent throughout the mixing of a project, some patches and settings might stay the same for every mix. Use recycled paper.

SETUP SHEET STORAGE

Once the mixes are logged, the setup sheets need to be stored in a safe place in case they are needed for a re-mix. Mix setup sheets can be quite bulky. Multiply the number of setup sheets by the 10 or 12 songs on the average project, and you have enough paperwork to sink the Bismarck — often too much to keep in the daily log. Perhaps keep them in a large manila envelope with the data disks and paperwork, and stored with the mix tapes.

BREAKING DOWN THE MIXES

After the mix is completely logged, the desk, patchbay, and outboard equipment need to be zeroed. Before starting the breakdown, double check with the engineer that he is finished with everything, then:

•   Start the mix breakdown at the patchbay, not at the desk. If any odd or unusual routing appears while breaking down the bay, the signal flow can still be traced at the desk.

- Remove each patchcord individually. Don't grab a handful of patches and yank, which is always a temptation. Use the engineer's patch list to check off each patchcord pulled, and see that the equipment settings on each unit are correctly logged. When all patches are pulled from the bay, and all changes on the setup sheet are checked, the sheet must be correct.

- Finally, if adhesive tape was used on the strip, save it by rolling it up like a regular roll of tape. Pull down all faders, zero the desk, and clean up as you would after any session.

SETTING UP A RE-MIX

Setting up a re-mix ought to take around an hour, depending on how complicated the original mix was:

1) Bring all the outboard equipment used in the original mix into the control room. Plug in and turn on all the equipment.

2) If possible, label the desk with the adhesive strip used on the original mix. If it isn't available, re-label the strip on the desk using the list on the setup sheet.

3) Load the correct multitrack tapes on their machines. Patch the timecode tracks into the synchronizer, and load any offsets or VSOs noted on the setup sheet.

4) If a computer recall was used, find the corresponding setup and re-set the desk. If no computer was used, every single knob on the desk must be re-set.

5) Once the desk is properly set, make the crosspatches according to fig. 11.4. When the crosspatches are completed, play the tape to check that all tracks returning to the desk from the multitrack machine correspond to the strip on the desk.

6) Patch in the outboard equipment and label each unit, as was done for the original. Match the outboard equipment with the settings written down, front and back.

7) Set the center section of the desk with the correct master send and return levels.

8) When you have finished all the patching, play the tape again and check all outboard equipment for proper input level, signal flow, master levels, and returns.

9) Load any samples used on the original mix.

10) When you feel you have gotten the desk and outboard equipment back to the original mix, load the original mix on the mixdown machine. Play the original mix and your re-mix off the desk, starting both versions at exactly the same time, so that you hear song continuity as you A/B between the original mix and the new mix. This is one of the few chances you have at this stage in your career to use your ears. Listen to each instrument in the mix for level, effects, equalization, limiting, and overall differences. If you hear any inconsistencies between the original and the re-mix, go back to your setup sheet and trace the signal path.

FINAL ASSEMBLY

Song order is always a discussion toward the end of a project. Most artists try various combinations of song orders before deciding on which works best. They put a lot of effort into finding a favorable flow of emotion from the start of the recording to the end. Some artists prefer a favorable flow of money, and simply put the best songs first.

All final mixes need to be tight leadered, timed, and assembled on master reels. Traditionally, at 30 ips, half the analog final mixes fit on one large 12" reel, and the other half on another large 12" reel. Digital tapes hold much more program, so one tape should hold all the final mixes. Many engineers today mix directly to a hard drive computer, do all the editing and tight leadering on the computer, then record the mixes onto DAT.

LABELING THE FINAL MIX TAPE

On the master mix tape label, write the individual song titles, times, and the total playing time. Write the correct time on the master reel label, along with the total playing time, side A and side B. All songs must be edited and tight leadered before the total playing time is established.

Make safety masters of all master mix reels as described in Chapter Nine. After making the safety masters, listen back from beginning to end. If there are any dropouts, the safety must be re-recorded.

Master tapes that leave the studio should always have typed labels, with all the applicable information as described in Chapter Eight. Most tapes for a commercially released project will be sent or taken to the mastering lab.

MASTERING

Mastering is the process of final equalization and level matching, done to make each song consistent with the other songs. Sometimes different songs within a project are mixed with different overall equalization. For example, the mix of one song might have more low end than another, or may be printed hotter to tape than the rest. The mastering engineer hears this, and adjusts them so all mixes sound consistent.

If possible, volunteer to take the final mixes to the mastering lab. This is an exceptional place for an eager assistant to really use his ears and hear what the mastering engineer is listening for. By now you should know how the mixes sound, so watch and listen to what the mastering engineer does.

. . . .

Summary

Chapter Eleven explained about what is expected of the assistant during mixdown:

- Setting up desk, and outboard and equipment to the engineers satisfaction.

- Running all tape machines.

- Keeping all paperwork organized throughout the mix, including detailed tape labels, and complete setup sheets for a re-mix.

- Helping print and edit the mixes. Making everyone a copy. Mastering.

CHAPTER TWELVE

. . . .

After The Session

The session ends when everything has been recorded, time has run out, everyone is too weary to continue, or technical problems force the session to stop. Contrary to popular belief, the session does not end when the assistant engineer decides he is tired.

Before everyone leaves, they will agree to the next session's start time, and what instrument and song to start with. Often, when the session is locked out, start times change from day to day. When the session is over, everyone gathers their belongings and prepares to leave, but there is still work for the assistant engineer.

THE CLIENT

WORK ORDER

The work order is the daily contract between the client and the recording studio and includes the session's events and costs. The producer agrees to the charges incurred by signing the daily work order. The work order is then handed in to the studio manager, who in turn, bills the client. Every studio uses work orders differently, so there isn't a standard way to complete them. Enclosed is an example of a work order. Figure 12.1.

		SONG TITLE/WORK DONE			
	(AEH)	MIXED "WIENER WATER SOUP BLUES"			
		STUDIO A ☐ STUDIO B ☒ COPY ROOM ☐ INVOICE:			

DATE AUG 3 —			CLIENT BLACK INK PUBLISHING. P. O. #		
TIME BOOKED			ADDRESS		
IN 11A OUT 11 P			ATTN.		
TIME USED			ARTIST/SESSION TUFF BEANS. PRODUCER W·GAINES		
IN 11A OUT 2:30 P			ENGINEER HERBIE HYNDE ASST. ENG. A·READER		
FORMAT: 24 TRACKS			ANALOG ☒ DIGITAL ☐ SUBTOTAL FWD.		

CONTROL ROOM			TOTALS	RENTALS & MISC.	
LOCKOUT	DAYS @ $	/DY			
RECORD	HRS @ $	/HR			
OVERDUB	HRS @ $	/HR		RENTED 3	
MIX	15.5 HRS @ $ 50	/HR		EQUALIZERS @ $50	$150
COPY	HRS @ $	/HR			
TRANSFER	HRS @ $	/HR			
COPY ROOM					
EDIT	HRS @ $	/HR			
LEADER	HRS @ $	/HR		TOTAL	
COPY	HRS @ $	/HR		% STATE/PROV. SALES TAX	
STOCK				FOOD/PHONE $30 —	
2" ANA.	@ $	/EACH		ADDL.	
DIG MULTI.	@ $	/EACH		SUBTOTAL	
1/2"	@ $	/EACH		PREV. BAL	
1/4"	@ $	/EACH		TOTAL	
DAT	@ $	/EACH		CLIENT APPROVAL W G	
CASS.	@ $	/EACH		ENGINEER APPROVAL	
	@ $	/EACH		HERBIE HYNDE	
		TOTAL			

Figure 12.1. Work Order

However the work order is designed, it should always contain:

- The name of the person or company paying the studio bill.

- The names of the artist, producer, engineer, assistant engineer and studio.

- The scheduled date and time of the session.

- Session events. Some studios use different rates for setting up, recording, overdubbing, and mixing. Include hours used and any session down time.

- General details of the session, with the names of songs and instruments recorded. Whoever pays the bill will want a daily breakdown, not simply the number of hours used.

- Number of tapes used, with their appropriate control numbers. (See later in this chapter for more on control numbers.)

- Additional rentals, such as microphones or outboard equipment.

- Any additional charges, such as food, taxis, or long distance telephone calls.

- Signatures. Make sure the producer or engineer signs the work order after every session. Sometimes, if the studio is booked out for a long project, days may go by without getting the work order signed. When the producer finally goes to sign them all, he invariably questions the hours or equipment indicated. With the work order signed after every session, any discrepancies of charges or hours used can be discussed while still fresh in everyone's mind.

- All events that occurred during the session, along with any technical problems, the next session's start time, and any information you feel the manager might need.

PAYMENT

Usually the bill gets sent from the studio to the money people. These may be the record company, the ad agency, the jingle house or simply the financial backers. The financial, or billing section of the work order is usually completed by the studio manager. If the client is paying after the session, and the manager is not there, you will have to deal with the payment. Follow these steps:

1) Work out all the details and costs for the session, and completely fill in the work order. Of course, you will need to know the individual costs of everything, such as the studio rates, multitrack tape, cassettes, etc. If you don't know these costs, look for an itemized list somewhere on the premises.

2) Get the full payment from the client, *then* give him the receipt and a copy of the work order — not the other way around.

3) Put the payment, whether check or cash, in a safe place, such as in the manager's desk, or in the studio safe. Find out which is studio policy.

4) If there are any discrepancies regarding costs, call the studio manager. Don't get into discussions with the client over misunderstandings on the work order. Better to telephone the studio manager at 2 A.M. and straighten everything out before the client leaves with the tapes, than hunt the client down the next day to get more money. Red tape and audio tape simply don't mix.

SESSION BREAKDOWN

After the work order is signed, and everyone else has left, you can begin the studio breakdown. With a runner helping, the job will be much easier. If you are completing the last session of the day, you should be able to take your time while breaking down.

If there is another session right after yours, break down the control room first, so the engineer for the next session can get started. It might be helpful to the assistant on the next session to leave anything he needs set up, such as specific microphones, headphones or baffles.

Before starting the breakdown, check that everything is properly documented. Depending on the session, you may have to write down the settings of equipment in the control room and the studio.

TAPES

Remove any tapes from the machines, and place them in their proper boxes. Scan the control room for any tracksheets and put them with the tapes.

Leaving tapes loaded on a machine overnight is not recommended. When a tape *must* be left loaded overnight, loosen the tension from the capstan path to ease pressure on the springs and to relax the relays. Of course, this is not an issue with digital multitrack cassettes. If you are working on the same song tomorrow, and no other session is scheduled in between, wind the tape off the machine without changing the counter number reset. When you return tomorrow, you should be able to load the same tape and wind directly to your spot. If the person checking the alignment doesn't change the counter numbers, they will stay consistent.

Common practice is to return all tapes to the vault after the session. Insurance policies in most studios dictate that all tapes not in active use must be safely stored in a cool dry room. If all the tapes are in the control room and anything happens, such as a flood, the tapes might not be covered by insurance. They would, however, be covered with water.

Vault/Control Numbers

The vault, or tape library, is where all tapes are stored. Never take any unauthorized person into the vault, because this is how cassettes and DATs mysteriously vanish.

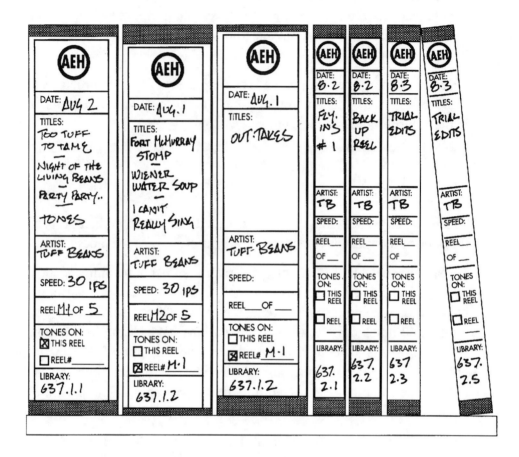

Figure 12.2. Reels Organized By Control Number

In major studios many different tapes of different formats go through at a regular pace. No matter how large or small, the vault must be organized in a way to keep track of all tapes. All incoming and outgoing reels, past, present, and future projects, virgin reels and tapes of different formats will need to be organized and numbered. With a large vault, a reliable system is needed.

The Dewey Decimal System, named after that wacky librarian Melvil Dewey, is a numbering system used to organize many similar items with different and varied categories. With this system, all non-virgin tapes are given a control number, and can be continually updated within a project. For example, if the project is numbered 637, multitrack tapes are numbered 637.1.1., 637.1.2. etc. while ½" tapes are numbered 637.2.1., 637.2.2., etc. Figure 12.2. Virgin tapes aren't usually given control numbers until they are used, or assigned to a project.

Tapes Leaving The Studio

Master tapes always stay at the studio until the bill is fully paid, or an arrangement has been made with the studio manager. If the client is a regular at the studio, he may have a degree of leeway, but unless you have specific authorization, never release any tapes to anyone, including the musicians. Possession of the master tapes is the studio's only real guarantee that the client will pay his outstanding debt. If the studio has no tapes to hold until full payment, there is little that the studio can do when the client doesn't live up to his financial obligations.

Tape Control Forms

Tape control forms are used to organize the many tapes that come and go through the studio. These forms contain the control numbers, the titles, the format, where the tapes originated, and their destination. Figure 12.3. All tapes, except cassettes, are logged upon arrival, and given a control number.

Whenever tapes leave the studio, make sure the person receiving the tapes signs these forms. These tapes are the result of countless hours of work, and are a serious financial investment. While the studio is usually only responsible for the raw tape costs if they are lost or stolen, the damage comes in its reputation. A studio that loses tapes won't get many recommendations from unsatisfied customers.

(AEH)   TAPE CONTROL

TAPES INCOMING					
DATE	ARTIST	# OF TAPES	FORMAT	CTL NUMBER	SIGNATURE
AUG.6	BOURBON COWBOYS	7	2"	648.1.1	
				648.1.2	
				648.1.3	
				648.1.4	
				648.1.5	
				648.1.6	
				648.1.7	
		2	1/2"	648.2.1	
				648.2.2	
		3	1/4"	648.3.1	
				648.3.2	
				648.3.3	*(signature)*

TAPES OUTGOING					
DATE	ARTIST	# OF TAPES	FORMAT	CTL NUMBER	SIGNATURE
AUG.6.	TUFF BEANS	5	2"	637.1.1	
				637.1.2	
				637.1.3	
				637.1.4	
				637.1.5	
		4	1/2"	637.2.1	
				637.2.2	
				637.2.3	
				637.2.4	
		3	1/4	637.3.1	
				637.3.2	
				637.3.3	*(signature)*

Figure 12.3. Tape Control Form

Transporting Tapes

Tapes often need to be sent out, either up the street, over town, across the nation or around the world. When master tapes are going out, safety masters must be made first. However, safety masters aren't needed if a project has already been released. In other words, if the product is already in the stores, don't make the safeties.

When safeties for multitrack tapes are being made, check that all the tracksheets and tape labels are legible and correct. Write a note telling the assistant who receives the tapes to telephone you if there are any questions about the project. Fill out the tape release forms and have them ready to be signed by whoever is receiving them.

Put these tapes in their original cardboard shipping box and wrap them up in heavy paper then clearly mark the destination. If the tapes are just going across town then probably a runner from either your studio or the other studio will take them. If the tapes are going out of town, their value probably warrants them being sent via a reliable courier service. Mailing may not be not the best way to send tapes, no matter how well insured they may be.

CONTROL ROOM

Once the tapes have been dealt with, continue with the breakdown of the rest of the control room:

- If required, double check that all desk and outboard settings are correctly documented, either by computer or by the age old way of writing the settings down on paper. If applicable, make backup data disks containing all information before breaking down the desk.

- Sometimes the engineer will want certain channels on the desk left set up. If so, ask the assistant on the next session if it is possible that these channels not be used. When your session returns the next day, these channels will still retain their original settings.

- Zero the rest of the desk and the outboard equipment. Remove all cords from the patchbay, and clean all pencil marks and any adhesive tape off the desk.

- Store any samples or computer information from the session to its proper storage format — this may be to analog tape, digital tape, or a non-volatile storage device.

- Clean up any ashtrays, empty soda cans, coffee cups, and other trash. Sometimes clients accidentally leave little things behind, so mark such items with the owner's name and keep them with the tapes or equipment.

- If there are any technical problems or pertinent information regarding anything in the studio that may affect the session after yours, leave a note for the next assistant.

- Again, when the sessions are locked out everything usually stays the same for the next day's recording. If the setup is left overnight, write down the sounds that are still in use, such as an unfinished overdub, in case something gets changed after everyone has left. Invisible studio gremlins have been known to vaporize in the gloom of night and mischievously change a favorite setting. For some reason, things may not sound exactly the same the next day.

- Leave a "Do Not Touch" sign for the cleaning staff or anyone else who may enter the studio. Perhaps even run a long strip of adhesive tape from one corner of the desk to the other, and again the other way, creating a large ominous X over the desk.

- Finally, if it is studio policy, turn off all the equipment, starting with the amplifiers. Then turn off the tape machines, the television, and everything else in the control room, as per studio procedure. If there are keyboards or computers left on, check before you turn them off. Massive amounts of important information can be lost with an innocent flick of the "off" switch.

• Collect up all the lyrics, sheet music and all other paperwork left behind. Never leave lyrics behind for the people in the next session to throw away, or worse, read, or worse yet, use on their project. If someone in the session writes or draws something brilliant and leaves it behind, save it in a safe place so it won't get thrown out.

Keep every stray piece of paper such as drawings, notes, additional lyrics and ideas. For example, years ago after a Beatles session, a scrap of paper containing the original handwritten lyrics to one of their songs was almost thrown in the trash. Figure 12.4.

Figure 12.4. Original Lyrics Almost Thrown In The Trash

Not really, but hopefully you will think before you casually toss away seemingly unimportant scraps of paper.

STUDIO

Check with the engineer before breaking down the studio, as sometimes he will want certain instruments left up. Setups are sometimes left up and the next session works around them. For example, if the next session is a mixdown session, and your session is returning tomorrow to continue basics, the studio is left as is.

The recommended way to break down the studio is to start with the cables. If you start with the microphones, once you move them, the sounds are gone. If you start with the cables, the client still has a little time to mull over the latest recording. If he listens to the song with the new overdub a few times while you are breaking down the cables, and decides he isn't happy with a certain track, it can be re-recorded. As the microphones will still be up, the sound will be still there after simply plugging the cables back into the input panel.

Cables

Due to the manufacturing process, cables have a natural coil when wound. If you wrap the cable under your arm, like so much rope, it winds in only one direction. When it is unwound, it does so only in one direction, causing it to coil up like a garden hose. The correct way is to wrap it up in an inward-outward motion. This way, it is wound and unwound the same way with no looping in one direction, and no tangles. Figure 12.5. To wrap a cable, follow these steps:

1) Grasp the female end in one hand, leaving a bit dangling. With the other hand, grasp the cable and wind one loop over your first hand. The length of the loop should be about the distance from your hand to your elbow.

2) Then with your other hand, grasp the longer part of the cable about three feet (one meter) down.

3) Twist the wrist outward, creating an opposing loop with the long end of the cable.

IMPROPERLY WOUND CABLE
(IN ONE DIRECTION)

PROPERLY WOUND CABLE
(INWARD- OUTWARD TECHNIQUE)

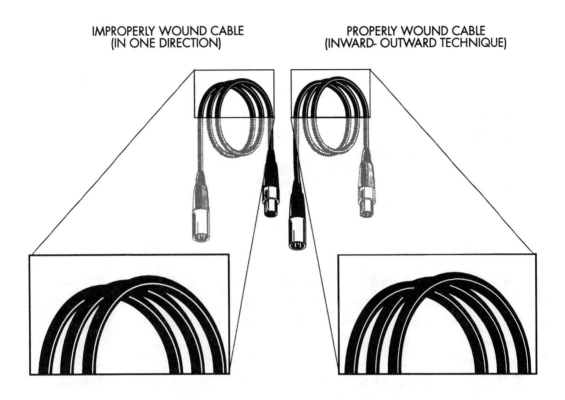

Figure 12.5. Wound Cables

4) Place this loop in hand one. Go back to step 1 winding the next loop inward. This repeats the inward-outward looping of a cable until it is completely wound.

Start wrapping the cable by unplugging it at the microphone end. Then when the cable is fully wound, you have the male jack at the end of the wound cable. The next time you use the cable, plug it in at the wall, and unravel as you walk to the microphone stand. The cable will unwind with the same inward-outward direction, and any excess cable will be left at the stand, in case the microphone needs to be moved.

Warning: Don't plug in a cable, then toss the remaining cable toward the microphone stand, unraveling as it goes. If tossed and unraveled incorrectly, the so-called "tosser" will get a cable full of knots.

After wrapping the cable, connect both ends to each other. Some studios tie a knot with one end of the cable to keep it together, but this is hard on the cable. Hold the cable together with a proper cable tie. Don't use masking tape, as it easily tears, and leaves a sticky coating.

Put the cables back in the correct spot in the cable room, as you may be the one who uses the cables next time.

Microphones

Breakdown of microphones occurs throughout the session, not just at the end of it. The assistant often needs to set up for another recording situation during the session. Breaking down microphones is the same as setting them up, only reversed:

- Remove the microphones from the stands. Put the microphones away two at a time with one in each hand.

- Some studios leave the microphones on the stands with the XLR cable. When you need one, you just grab the complete setup.

- Count the microphones as you put them away. Unfortunately, smaller pieces of expensive equipment may sometimes "accidentally" drop into someone's pocket. Counting equipment after every session is simply good business.

Microphones are the basic building blocks of a good sounding recording studio and, when well maintained, will remain in top notch condition for years.

Headphone Boxes, Tuners, Direct Boxes

After all the microphones and cables are put away, collect all the headphones. Then collect the smaller items, like headphone boxes, direct boxes, tuners, and put them away. Separate the studio items from the musicians' items, and don't let any musicians leave without all their equipment. All studio items should be well marked with studio's name.

Instruments

After all the smaller items are put away, the larger items, such as the drums, amplifiers, and any other musical instruments need to be dealt with. Studio musical equipment will need to be put away, even if it is into the corner. Usually though, the musicians will break down and take their instruments with them.

The Rest Of The Room

- Finally, straighten up all boom stands, and return microphone stands to their proper home. Remove any adhesive tape that may have been put on a stand during the session.

- Roll the baffles to their proper spot. Keep in mind that rolling a baffle over a stray cable is a great way to slice the cable in half.

- Stack the chairs in a corner.

- Roll up all carpets and rugs and put them in their proper places.

- Take any faulty equipment to the shop with a maintenance form explaining the problem.

- After cleaning up all the large items, sweep the floor and organize the studio. You are tidying up for the next assistant, so if he finds it messy, chances are, you'll find it that way after his session. The studio should now be as clean as it can be, and ready for the next session.

THE NEXT SESSION

When there is no session in after you, like late at night, you may be responsible for locking up the studio. Check that everything in the control room is off, all tapes are put away, and all the paperwork is complete and where it's supposed to be. Turn off the air conditioner, heaters, photocopy machine, computers, printers, and especially the coffee machine. Turn out all the lights, shut all the doors, and lock all the windows. When all this is done, you can set the burglar alarm, close up shop, and stagger home. But will you?

Everything has been cleaned and ready for tomorrow's first session. It's quarter to three and there's no one here but you and me. Let's sit at the desk and discuss an important issue.

LEARNING, THE OLD FASHIONED WAY

After the clients, the producer and the engineer leave, you and the late night staff (often only a runner or two) might be the only ones there. Some over-eager assistants may find a multitrack tape, load it on the machine and experiment. You aren't supposed to do this, but how else does one really learn to engineer.

If you stay late after a session, or even sneak into the studio at 3 A.M. and start experimenting with the desk and outboard equipment, what is the worst thing that can happen? Chances are, if you get caught, you will be reprimanded. So tell the truth. The engineer you work with was using a certain piece of equipment in a way that you didn't understand. To do your job effectively, you must know the complete workings of each piece of equipment, so you stayed late, on your own time, to investigate.

An eager assistant, armed with the vast amounts of information enclosed in this handbook, will be of such use to any studio that employs him, that he will be too valuable a staff member to be fired. The gains from experimenting are uncountable. The only way to learn it is to do it. Better to ask for forgiveness than permission. Here are a few thoughts on the subject:

- Don't use the client's tape or tapes from any important session unless you are authorized. If you erase, lose, or damage anything on tape, the studio will be rightfully held responsible, and you could easily lose your job. Find an old unclaimed or house tape.

- Don't bring in your band and record your own songs. If you get caught working on your project, this will be viewed as taking advantage of the studio for your own musical career. The main objective here is to learn the equipment by engineering, not becoming a rock star at the studio's expense. Mind you, it did work for Jon Bon Jovi. The songs you work on should be secondary to the learning process.

- Don't bring in your friends after hours to let them hear the project you are working on. Sure, it's great to impress the babes, but it gets you fired.

ENGINEERING

The term *recording engineer* refers to the person who gets the sounds. He chooses the tape, the microphones, the outboard, the equalization, and the track layout of all instruments. But simply understanding signal flow and recording techniques is not all it takes to be a good recording engineer. He also must be able to effectively deal with, and get the best out of, sometimes temperamental and egotistical musicians. He must be diplomatic in resolving disputes, and he must be easygoing enough to not get frustrated when things aren't going smoothly. He also has to know how to drink lots of coffee and wear loud Hawaiian shirts.

The Ladder

The main goal of the assistant engineer is to move up the recording studio ladder. The fastest way to do this is to think like an engineer, and take over the session. If you are always right there on top of everything, keeping up with the engineer, continually watching and helping, the client will notice this. Soon the producer may not want to spend the extra money hiring a big gun engineer, when he knows that you are available, competent, eager, and most importantly, cheap. Producers are always looking for eager young engineers who know their way around a studio. But remember, if they let you engineer, they let other assistants engineer.

Some engineers may be very intimidated by a good assistant who reads all the manuals and books, understands all the equipment, and makes very few mistakes. However, most engineers are happy to help an aspiring assistant.

Many engineers are dipping their toes in the sea of production, and will need good engineers. If you are on the ball, get on well with people, and do a good job, you may get one of these jobs. When you are called on to engineer, remember two things: do everything right, and do everything fast. You may be the best assistant in town, but sitting in the driver's seat and doing the engineering is a whole new ball game.

The Big Break

Many assistants get their first big break when the main engineer has to leave a session early, or fails to show up at all. This usually leaves the assistant to engineer the session. Studios sometimes rent out cheap time during off hours for lower budget projects, such as demos and house projects. Often, the rate given for the cheaper projects includes an engineer. An assistant is given the engineering job because he doesn't charge a lot, and really wants to do it.

Toward the end of a project, time restrictions may require another engineer to complete the overdubs. While the main engineer starts mixing, the trusted assistant is occasionally used to engineer some of the overdubs. This usually only happens if the premises has more than one studio.

RECORD CREDITS AND YOU

Credits are amazingly good for getting work as an engineer. If you do any engineering at all on a project, talk to the producer about an "Engineering" or even "Additional Engineering" credit. Although credits are important for your career as an engineer, the guidelines for credits are vague. There will be times you work on a project for a great length of time, yet not see your name on a final release. On the other hand, you may work on a project for a day, and get a great credit. Points to remember:

- An "Engineer" credit is better than an "Assistant Engineer" credit.

- An "Assistant Engineer" credit is better than being in the "Thank You" column.

- Anything is better than being in the "This Idiot Erased The Vocal Track" column.

KEEP IN CONTACT

Establish and maintain contacts with key producers and engineers. They deal with assistant engineers all the time, so show them that you want to be remembered, maybe even hired as an engineer in the future.

THE END

I hope you get as much pleasure out of using this book as I had writing it. Working in a recording studio can be a very rewarding career, and I sincerely hope you do well. Thank you very much, and good luck.

. . . .

Summary

Chapter Twelve explained about what is expected of the assistant engineer after the session ends:

- Dealing with the client after the session, including filling in the work order, and receiving payment.

- Putting all tapes away and, if the client is taking tapes, filling in the tape control forms.

- Breaking down the control room and studio after the session.

- Working your way up to engineer.

TITLE:
ARTIST:
PRODUCER:
ENGINEER:
CLIENT:

☐ 48 TK   ☐ 32 TK   ☐ 24 TK   ☐ 16 TK   ☐ 8 TK

1		2		3		4	
DATE:	MIC:	DATE:	MIC:	DATE:	MIC:	DATE:	MIC:
ENG:	STUDIO:	ENG:	STUDIO:	ENG:	STUDIO:	ENG:	STUDIO:
9		10		11		12	
DATE:	MIC:	DATE:	MIC:	DATE:	MIC:	DATE:	MIC:
ENG:	STUDIO:	ENG:	STUDIO:	ENG:	STUDIO:	ENG:	STUDIO:
17		18		19		20	
DATE:	MIC:	DATE:	MIC:	DATE:	MIC:	DATE:	MIC:
ENG:	STUDIO:	ENG:	STUDIO:	ENG:	STUDIO:	ENG:	STUDIO:

DATE:	TAPE:	SPEED: ☐ 30 IPS ☐ 15 IPS ☐ DIGITAL
STUDIO: ☐ A ☐ B ☐ C		N. R.: ☐ DOLBY ☐ DBX ☐ _____
REEL: OF:		SAMPLING RATE: ☐ 48 K ☐ 44.1 K
TONES ON REEL _____ ☐ HEAD ☐ TAIL		REF: _____ nWm = 0VU ☐ NAB ☐ IEC
ASSISTANT ENGINEER:		

☐ 4 TK ☐ MASTER ☐ SAFETY ☐ SLAVE ☐ CLONE

5	6	7	8
DATE:	MIC:	DATE:	MIC:	DATE:	MIC:	DATE:	MIC:
ENG:	STUDIO:	ENG:	STUDIO:	ENG:	STUDIO:	ENG:	STUDIO:

13	14	15	16
DATE:	MIC:	DATE:	MIC:	DATE:	MIC:	DATE:	MIC:
ENG:	STUDIO:	ENG:	STUDIO:	ENG:	STUDIO:	ENG:	STUDIO:

21	22	23	24
DATE:	MIC:	DATE:	MIC:	DATE:	MIC:	DATE:	MIC:
ENG:	STUDIO:	ENG:	STUDIO:	ENG:	STUDIO:	ENG:	STUDIO:

SONG TITLE/WORK DONE	
STUDIO A ☐ STUDIO B ☐ COPY ROOM ☐ INVOICE:	

DATE	CLIENT	P. O. #
TIME BOOKED	ADDRESS	
1N OUT		ATTN.
TIME USED	ARTIST/SESSION	PRODUCER
1N OUT	ENGINEER	ASST. ENG.
FORMAT: TRACKS	ANALOG ☐ DIGITAL ☐	SUBTOTAL FWD.

CONTROL ROOM			TOTALS	RENTALS & MISC.	
LOCKOUT	DAYS @ $	/DY			
RECORD	HRS @ $	/HR			
OVERDUB	HRS @ $	/HR			
MIX	HRS @ $	/HR			
COPY	HRS @ $	/HR			
TRANSFER	HRS @ $	/HR			
COPY ROOM					
EDIT	HRS @ $	/HR			
LEADER	HRS @ $	/HR		TOTAL	
COPY	HRS @ $	/HR		% STATE/PROV. SALES TAX	
STOCK				FOOD/PHONE	
2" ANA.	@ $	/EACH		ADDL.	
DIG MULTI.	@ $	/EACH		SUBTOTAL	
1/2"	@ $	/EACH		PREV. BAL	
1/4"	@ $	/EACH		TOTAL	
DAT	@ $	/EACH		CLIENT APPROVAL	
CASS.	@ $	/EACH			
	@ $	/EACH		ENGINEER APPROVAL	
		TOTAL			

ARTIST _____ DATE _____

PRODUCER _____ STUDIO ☐ A ☐ B ☐ C

ENGINEER _____ ASSISTANT _____

INSTRUMENT	MICROPHONE	PARAMETER	INPUT	BUSS	OUTBOARD

DATE:	REEL:	OF:	☐ 30 IPS ☐ 15 IPS ☐ DIG.
ARTIST:			REFERENCE:_____ nWm = 0VU

DATE:

TITLES:

PRODUCER:	☐ 1K ☐ THIS REEL
ENGINEER:	☐ 10K ☐ REEL#_____
ASSISTANT:	☐ 15K ☐ RECORD PAD
	☐ 50 Hz ☐ HEAD ☐ TAIL
CLIENT:	☐ 100 Hz ☐ N. R._____

☐ MASTER   ☐ COPY
☐ SAFETY   ☐ CLONE

☐ 48TK   ☐ 32TK   ☐ 24TK   ☐ 16TK   ☐ 8TK   ☐ 2TK

ARTIST:

SPEED:

REEL____OF ____

TONES ON:
☐ THIS REEL
☐ REEL#_____

LIBRARY:

TITLES	TAKE	LOCATE / CTL	TIME	COMMENTS

FS - FALSE START	C - COMPLETE	HL - HEAD LEADER	TL - TAIL LEADER	HTL - HEAD AND TAIL LEADER
INC - INCOMPLETE	H - HOLD	HM - HEAD MARK	TM - TAIL MARK	HTM - HEAD AND TAIL MARK

DATE:	REEL:	OF:	☐ 30 IPS ☐ 15 IPS ☐ DIG.
ARTIST:			REFERENCE:_____ nWm = 0VU
PRODUCER:			☐ 1K ☐ THIS REEL
ENGINEER:			☐ 10K ☐ REEL#_____
ASSISTANT:			☐ 15K ☐ RECORD PAD
			☐ 50 Hz ☐ HEAD ☐ TAIL
CLIENT:			☐ 100 Hz ☐ N. R._____

☐ 48TK   ☐ 32TK   ☐ 24TK   ☐ 16TK   ☐ 8TK   ☐ 2TK

☐ MASTER   ☐ COPY
☐ SAFETY   ☐ CLONE

TITLES	TAKE	LOCATE / CTL	TIME	COMMENTS

FS - FALSE START	C - COMPLETE	HL - HEAD LEADER	TL - TAIL LEADER	HTL - HEAD AND TAIL LEADER
INC - INCOMPLETE	H - HOLD	HM - HEAD MARK	TM - TAIL MARK	HTM - HEAD AND TAIL MARK

MAINTENANCE REPORT NO.   DATE: _____

SESSION: _____   TIME: _____

ENGINEER: _____   STUDIO:

ASSISTANT: _____   ☐ A   ☐ B   ☐ C

SYMPTOMS PLEASE BE EXPLICIT - INCLUDE ENVIRONMENT OF PROBLEM

TEMPORARY ACTION TAKEN:

REPAIRED BY: _____   DATE: _____
DIAGNOSIS:

PARTS SENT OR ORDERED: _____   DATE: _____

PARTS RECEIVED: _____   DATE: _____

DELAY CHART IN MILLISECONDS

BPM	1/4	1/4 TRIP	1/8	1/8 TRIP	1/16	1/16 TRIP	1 BAR	2 BARS	4 BARS	8 BARS
80	750.0	500.0	375.0	250.0	187.5	125.0	3.000	6.111	12.000	24.000
81	740.7	493.8	370.4	246.9	185.2	123.5	2.963	5.926	11.852	23.704
82	731.7	487.8	365.9	243.9	182.9	122.0	2.927	5.854	11.707	23.415
83	722.9	481.9	361.4	241.0	180.7	120.5	2.892	5.783	11.566	23.133
84	714.3	476.2	357.1	238.1	178.6	119.0	2.857	5.714	11.429	22.857
85	705.9	470.6	352.9	235.3	176.5	117.6	2.824	5.647	11.294	22.588
86	697.7	465.1	348.8	232.6	174.4	116.3	2.791	5.581	11.163	22.326
87	689.7	459.8	344.8	229.9	172.4	114.9	2.759	5.517	11.034	22.069
88	681.8	454.5	340.9	227.3	170.5	113.6	2.727	5.455	10.909	21.818
89	674.2	449.4	337.1	224.7	168.5	112.4	2.697	5.393	10.787	21.574
90	666.7	444.4	333.3	222.2	166.7	111.1	2.667	5.333	10.667	21.333
91	659.3	439.6	329.7	219.8	164.8	109.9	2.637	5.275	10.549	21.099
92	652.2	434.8	326.1	217.4	163.0	108.7	2.609	5.217	10.435	20.870
93	645.2	430.1	322.6	215.1	161.3	107.5	2.581	5.161	10.323	20.645
94	638.3	425.5	319.1	212.8	159.6	106.4	2.553	5.106	10.213	20.426
95	631.6	421.1	315.8	210.5	157.9	105.3	2.526	5.053	10.105	20.211
96	625.0	416.1	312.5	208.3	156.3	104.2	2.500	5.000	10.000	20.000
97	618.6	412.4	309.3	206.2	154.6	103.1	2.474	4.948	9.897	19.794
98	612.2	408.2	306.1	204.1	153.1	102.0	2.449	4.898	9.796	19.592
99	606.1	404.0	303.0	202.0	151.5	101.0	2.424	4.848	9.697	19.394
100	600.0	400.0	300.0	200.0	150.0	100.0	2.400	4.800	9.600	19.200
101	594.1	396.0	297.0	198.0	148.5	99.0	2.376	4.752	9.505	19.010
102	588.2	392.2	294.1	196.1	147.1	98.0	2.354	4.706	9.412	18.824
103	582.5	388.3	391.3	194.2	145.6	97.1	2.330	4.660	9.320	18.641
104	576.9	384.6	288.5	192.3	144.2	96.2	2.308	4.615	9.231	18.462
105	571.4	381.0	285.7	190.5	142.9	95.2	2.286	4.571	9.143	18.286
106	566.0	377.4	283.0	188.7	141.5	94.3	2.264	4.528	9.057	18.113
107	560.7	373.8	280.4	186.9	140.2	93.5	2.243	4.486	8.972	17.944
108	555.6	370.4	277.8	185.2	138.9	92.6	2.222	4.444	8.889	17.778
109	550.5	367.0	275.2	183.5	137.6	91.7	2.202	4.404	8.807	17.616
110	545.5	363.6	272.7	181.8	136.4	90.9	2.192	4.364	8.727	17.455
111	540.5	360.4	270.3	180.2	135.1	90.1	2.162	4.324	8.649	17.297
112	535.7	357.1	267.9	178.6	133.9	89.3	2.143	4.286	8.571	17.143
113	531.0	354.0	265.5	177.0	132.7	88.5	2.124	4.248	8.496	16.991
114	526.3	350.9	263.2	175.4	131.6	87.7	2.105	4.211	8.421	16.842
115	521.7	347.8	260.9	173.9	130.4	87.0	2.087	4.174	8.348	16.696
116	517.2	344.8	258.6	172.4	129.3	86.2	2.069	4.138	8.276	16.552
117	512.8	341.9	256.4	170.9	128.2	85.5	2.051	4.103	8.205	16.410
118	508.5	339.0	254.2	169.5	127.1	84.7	2.034	4.068	8.136	16.271
119	504.2	336.1	252.1	168.1	126.1	84.0	2.017	4.034	8.067	16.134
120	500.0	333.3	250.0	166.7	125.0	83.3	2.000	4.000	8.000	16.000
121	496.8	331.5	248.0	165.5	123.9	82.7	1.984	3.968	7.936	15.872
122	492.5	327.9	246.3	163.9	123.0	81.9	1.962	3.936	7.872	15.744
123	488.2	325.3	244.2	162.6	122.1	81.3	1.952	3.904	7.808	15.616
124	484.0	322.6	242.0	161.3	121.3	80.6	1.936	3.872	7.744	15.488
125	480.1	319.9	240.1	159.6	120.0	79.8	1.920	3.840	7.680	15.360
126	475.9	317.3	238.2	158.6	119.2	79.3	1.904	3.808	7.616	15.232
127	472.1	314.6	236.9	157.3	118.4	78.6	1.888	3.776	7.552	15.104
128	469.5	312.6	234.5	156.3	117.2	78.1	1.876	3.752	7.504	15.008
129	465.0	309.9	232.5	154.9	116.2	77.4	1.860	3.720	7.440	14.880
130	462.0	307.9	231.0	153.9	115.5	76.9	1.848	3.696	7.392	14.784

INVENTORY SHEET   SESSION_____

STUDIO	DATE	2"	1/2"	1/4"	DIG. 1	DIG. 2	CASSETTES	DATS
		M	H	Q	A	B	C	D

CROSS-PATCHING

LINE IN	PROGRAM	SOURCE TRACK	TAPE MON IN	LINE IN	PROGRAM	SOURCE TRACK	TAPE MON IN
1				33			
2				34			
3				35			
4				36			
5				37			
6				38			
7				39			
8				40			
9				41			
10				42			
11				43			
12				44			
13				45			
14				46			
15				47			
16				48			
17				49			
18				50			
19				51			
20				52			
21				53			
22				54			
23				55			
24				56			
25				57			
26				58			
27				59			
28				60			
29				61			
30				62			
31				63			
32				64			

SENDS

SENDS	EFFECT	RETURNS
1		
2		
3		
4		
5		
6		
CUE L		
CUE R		

INSERTS

INS. OUT		INS. IN

BUSSING

BUSS	EFFECT	RETURN
1		
2		
3		
4		
5		
6		
7		
8		
9		
10		
11		
12		
13		
14		
15		
16		
17		
18		
19		
20		
21		
22		
23		
24		
25		
26		
27		
28		
29		
30		
31		
32		

INDEX

YES, I WANT THE ASSISTANT ENGINEERS HANDBOOK and RECORDING TIPS FOR ENGINEERS.

Please RUSH me_____copies of Assistant Engineers Handbook @$29.95 = $_____

Please RUSH me_____copies of Recording Tips For Engineers @$39.95 = $_____

Shipping and Handling @$3.00 per Book = $_____

Applicable Tax = $_____

Enclosed is a check or money order for = $_____

Thank you for the order!

Order toll free 1 800 265 8481. Visa m/c accepted.

Ship to:

Name:_____

Address:_____

City:_____Prov./State_____Code_____

Please Send this order form to:
Black ink Publishing
Post Office Box 4295
Dept F.
Vancouver CANADA V6B-3Z7

Please allow 2-3 weeks delivery.
Recording Tips For Engineers (ISBN 0-969-82231-6)
Assistant Engineers Handbook (ISBN 0-969-82230-8)
Discounts on bulk orders. Contact publisher at:
www.aehandbook.com Email: tcrich@intergate.ca
© 2001 Black ink Publishing. All rights reserved.

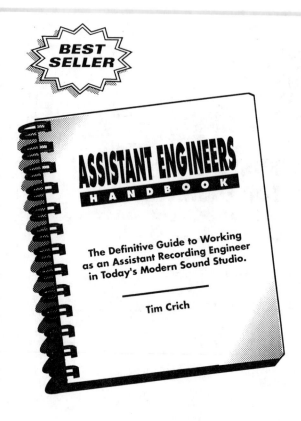

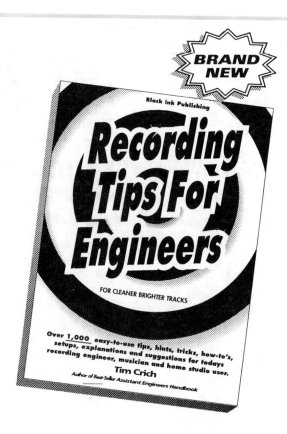

ASSISTANT ENGINEERS HANDBOOK

- Over 275 pages. Fully illustrated, 7" x 9" Wirebound.
- Packed with proven recording studio secrets.
- Complete setups for basics, overdubs and mixing.
- Proper microphone handling and setup.
- Most efficient ways to complete all paperwork.
- Needed pointers on recording studio etiquette.
- Established procedures to keep the session moving.
- Key priorities for before, during and after the session.
- Essential tips on setup and breakdown of all equipment.
- Full Chapter on tape machines and alignment.
- Required reading in Audio schools throughout North America.
- Much, much more!

RECORDING TIPS FOR ENGINEERS

- Over 300 pages, Fully Illustrated 7" x 10" Perfect bound.
- Pesky technical information kept to a minimum.
- Written in simple point form. No endless rambling.
- Established procedures to get the very best recordings.
- Proper microphone choice and final placement
- Effective equalization and compression methods.
- Key procedures for before, during and after recording.
- Huge Chapter on professional sounding mixes.
- Advance your career as a Recording Engineer.
- Includes easy to understand digital appendix.
- Dial in great sounds from any size recording studio.
- Much, much more!

ABOUT THE AUTHOR

Tim Crich began his career as an illustrator in Western Canada, but moved to New York to persue recording. With over twenty years experience in the recording studio, he has credits on some of the biggest records in history. He has engineered for many producers including Bob Rock, Bruce Fairbairn, Bob Clearmountain, Steve Lillywhite, many more. Tim Crich is a recording engineer and writer/illustrator living in Vancouver Canada.

See over for order form.